Reading in Content Areas

STRATEGIES FOR READING SUCCESS

Level A

Program Consultant
Dr. Kate Kinsella
San Francisco State University
San Francisco, California

Upper Saddle River, New Jersey
www.globefearon.com

Consultants

John Edwin Cowen, Ed.D.
Assistant Professor, Education/Reading
Program Coordinator, Graduate M.A.T./
Elementary Education
School of Education
Fairleigh Dickinson University
Teaneck, NJ

Dr. Kate Kinsella
Dept. of Secondary Education and
Step to College Program
San Francisco State University
San Francisco, CA

Reviewers

Bettye J. Birden
Reading Specialist
McReynolds Middle School
Houston, TX

Sally Parker, M.A.
T.R. Smedberg Middle School/
Sheldon High School
Elk Grove, Unified School District
Elk Grove, CA

Georgeanne Herbeck
District Supervisor, Elementary Education
Perth Amboy, NJ

Kenneth J. Ratti
Science Department Chairman
Vaca Peña Middle School
Vacaville, CA

Senior Editor: Lynn W. Kloss
Editor: Monica Glina
Editorial Assistant: Kevin Iwano
Writers: Sandra Widener, Terri Flynn-Nason
Production Editor: Alan Dalgleish
Cover and Interior Design: Lisa Nuland
Electronic Page Production: José López

Photo Credits
p. 6: Courtesy of MacGillivray Freeman Film; **p. 10:** The Museum of Modern Art/Film Still Archive; **p. 13:** Richard Hutchins, Photo Researchers; **p. 14:** Ken Cavanaugh, Photo Researchers; **p. 19:** UPI/Corbis-Bettmann; **p. 23:** AP/WideWorld; **p. 30:** US Patent Office; **p. 31:** US Patent Office; **p. 34:** Brian Bahn/Allsport; **p. 37:** Photofest; **p. 38:** Photofest; **p. 38:** (top and bottom) Photofest; **p. 49:** The Library of Congress; **p. 59:** Trevor Ray Hart-Katz/Matrix International, Inc.; **p. 73:** National Oceanic and Atmospheric Administration/Seattle; **p. 95:** Spencer Grant, Photo Researchers; **p. 105:** AP/WideWorld Photos; **p. 111:** Jeff Greenberg, Photo Researchers

Printed in the United States of America   6 7 8 9 10   04 03 02 01
ISBN: 0-835-94917-6

1-800-848-9500
www.globefearon.com

Contents

To the Student

The Hows and Whys of Reading

Think of a story that you've read. Maybe it was about someone's exciting adventure. What did you want to know about the story? What kinds of questions did you ask to get that information?

If you were reading an adventure story, you probably wanted to know *who* the characters were and *when* and *where* they were going. These questions are very helpful when reading *literary text,* which includes things like short stories, novels, plays, and myths. They all tell a story.

There is another kind of writing that is called *informational text.* This kind of writing informs the reader by giving opinions, explanations, reasons, facts, and examples about a certain topic. Things like chapters in a textbook and newspaper articles are considered informational text, so you are already familiar with this type of writing.

Good Questions for Literary Text	Good Questions for Informational Text
who	how
when	what
where	why

Think back to an example of literary text you've read. How are the questions you ask about a story different from the ones you ask when you read a chapter in your science book? In a science book, the questions *how, what,* and *why* are a great way to ask the "big" questions and get the information you are looking for. You might even start by changing the bold type headings and topic sentences into questions that begin with *how, what,* and *why.* Since *who, where* and *when* can be answered with a simple fact or one-word answer, they are not as useful when reading informational text. Look at the following example:

Heading		Question
Promoting Economic Growth	*becomes*	How can you promote economic growth?
Causes of Earthquakes	*becomes*	What causes earthquakes?
The Protests Affect U.S. Policy	*becomes*	Why do the protests affect U.S. policy?

These are examples of "big" questions. It is by asking these big questions that you will get the most out of the informational texts that you read. In this book, you'll learn more strategies for reading informational text and for remembering what you read.

Unit 1
Using Reading Strategies

Although you may not know it, you may already use a strategy when you read. Here's an example. You look at a magazine cover. A headline catches your eye. You see a picture of a musician or style of clothing you like. Then you look at the table of contents. Does an article sound interesting? If it does, you turn to that page. You look at a photograph in the article. Then you read the caption under it. You read the article. After you read, you think about what you have read. You have just used a reading strategy.

A reading strategy is a plan that helps you understand the information you read. The reading strategies in this book can help you understand readings in language arts, social studies, science, and math. They can also help you understand things you read in your life outside of school or at a job. You will be able to link what you are reading to what you already know. Reading strategies will also help you remember what you read.

Becoming an Active Reader

When you use a strategy for reading, you take an active part in reading. You respond to the reading with thoughts, questions, and ideas. You also respond by taking notes or summarizing what you read. Finally, you think about what you read. What these steps have in common is that you are involved with what you are reading.

Steps of the Strategies

Although different strategies work well for different kinds of reading, all the strategies in this book have three steps in common. You preview. Then you read and take notes. Finally, you review. Below is a drawing of the steps of the reading strategies.

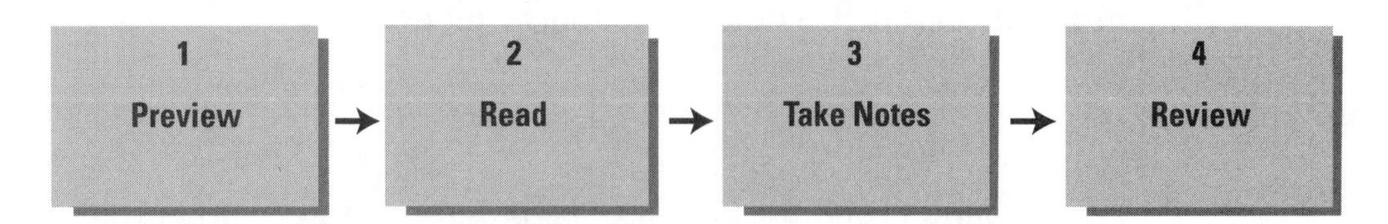

First, think about what you will read. In every strategy, you preview what you will read by skimming. When you skim, you don't want to go too deep. You want to skim the surface to get an idea of what you will be reading about.

Here are the steps to use when you preview:

1. Look at the title. What clues does it give you about the topic?
2. Look at the illustrations or diagrams and read the captions. Often, major points are illustrated.
3. Read the first paragraph. It may include a summary of what is to come.
4. Read the last paragraph. It may sum up the writer's main points.
5. Read the first sentence of every paragraph. It will give you hints on what you will read.

Second, read carefully. As you read, think about what you are reading. What is the author telling you? Do you understand all of the words you are reading? Look for clues that the author has given you.

Third, take notes. The kind of notes you take will vary depending on what you are reading. A researcher found that students remember only 5 to 34 percent of the information they don't take notes on. When you take notes, you put information in your own words. That helps the information stay in your mind.

Fourth, review what you have read. You may review a section in a math textbook by working problems to see if you understand the concept. Often, though, you will want to write a summary. When you write a summary, you put the author's thoughts into your own words. You review the main points of the reading and the details that support these main points.

Choosing a Strategy

There are a variety of strategies in this book because people learn—and read—in different ways. After trying different strategies, you might find that one always works best for you. You may also find that one strategy works better on one type of reading. For example, one strategy might work well on an article on how to make a poster. Another strategy might work well on a debate about movie ratings.

Experiment with these strategies. You'll find that you can use them on any reading you have, both in school and out of school. You'll also find that they'll help you make sense of your reading—and remember it!

Strategy 1 KWL Plus

Understand It..... Active readers approach reading with a strategy. They think about what they will read. They have an idea of *why* they are reading. After they read, they figure out whether they understand what they have read. KWL Plus (**K**now, **W**ant to Know, **L**earned) is one way of putting all those ideas to work for you. The summary is the **Plus** part of the strategy.

Try It.............. Look at the sample KWL chart below that one student made. The reading was a newspaper article describing a movie about climbing Mount Everest.

Step 1. Write the main points of what you already know about this topic.

Thinking about what you already know helps you focus your mind. You'll also find that remembering something new is easier if you can connect it to information you already know.

The student started this KWL chart before she read the article about climbing Mount Everest. She wrote information she already knew. Add two things you know about mountain climbing or about Mount Everest to the K section of this chart.

K (What I know)	W (What I want to know)	L (What I've learned)
Lots of snow and ice Dangerous conditions		

Step 2. Write what you want to know.

Now that you've listed things you know, think about what you'd like to learn about mountain climbing and about Mount Everest. Questions that begin with *what, why,* and *how* work well because they help you look for the important points of an article. Questions that begin with *who, where,* and *when* are less useful because they usually talk about one small point.

Here are some questions that the student thought about as she previewed the article:

Why is mountain climbing such a big adventure?

How hard is it to climb a mountain?

Why was this climb so difficult?

Now preview the article, looking at the topic sentences of each paragraph. Use this information to write questions about mountain climbing. Your questions can help you prepare for reading by giving you a reason to read—to find answers. The questions can also help you organize what you read.

Read the questions the student wrote in the W section of the KWL chart below. Then add two questions you have about mountain climbing.

K (What I know)	W (What I want to know)	L (What I've learned)
Lots of snow and ice Dangerous conditions	What are the dangers of mountain climbing? How does the weather affect climbing?	

Step 3. Write what you learn.

After you read this passage, write what you learn about mountain climbing in the L section of the KWL chart. Try to write the facts that answer questions you wrote in the W section. You may not find the answers to all your questions in this article. If you don't find them, check another book or article on mountain climbing or on Mount Everest. If you can, you might even look on the Internet.

Strategy Tip

Thinking about why you are reading helps you focus your reading. For example, if you need information for a report, make up a list of questions or topics. Then look for that information while you read.

Climbing to the Top of the World

Mountain climbing is one of the last great adventures on Earth. At 29,029 feet (8,848 meters), Mount Everest is the greatest of all climbing challenges. The air contains little oxygen. People have trouble breathing. Thinking is difficult. Very few people have reached the top. Even today, with all the technology on Earth, Everest is one place that cannot be tamed.

Mountain climbing is hard enough. Now think about climbing while backpacking heavy equipment. David Breashears and his camera crew faced that chore in 1996. Their job was to make a film for IMAX about Everest and the people who dare to climb it.

The climb itself turned out to be the least of the filmmakers' problems. The day they were to go up the mountain, many other climbers were also preparing to tackle Everest. The weather did not look good, so the IMAX crew decided to wait. The wind howled, and snow blew. The IMAX team listened in horror to the mountaineers above them. Stuck on the summit, the climbers were dying in the deadly storm.

David Breashears and his crew climb Mt. Everest.

Many other photographers would have begun shooting film. The IMAX crew members responded differently. They dropped their equipment. Desperately, they tried to save lives. In the end, eight people died in the 1996 tragedy.

Later, saddened by their experience, the IMAX crew members shot their film. The camera shows the filmmakers helping victims into helicopters. Viewers see the IMAX team members fight back tears. Then they turn around and climb to the top.

On their way up, the team members walk past the bodies of the climbers who died. At the summit, the world spreads out below them. It is a calm world of crystal and blue. Their movie, *Everest*, shows the deadly dangers—and the breathtaking beauty—of mountain climbing.

"[The movie is] incredible," said one man who had climbed Everest. "It's as close as you can get to doing it yourself." At one point, a cameraman teeters across an aluminum bridge. He is lugging his camera over a deep **crevasse**.

Vocabulary Tip

Look at clues in the paragraph to figure out what *crevasse* means. A bridge goes across it and it is deep. A crevasse is like a canyon.

Everest is a movie about life and death. It is about the urge that drives people to go where no one should go. Finally, it is about a mountain that will always be bigger than those who climb it. The struggle—and the beauty—makes climbers want to tame mountains.

On the L section of the KWL chart on page 7 are the notes the student wrote after she finished the article. Add your own notes to the L section of this chart.

K (What I know)	W (What I want to know)	L (What I've learned)
Lots of snow and ice Dangerous conditions	What are the dangers of mountain climbing? How does the weather affect climbing?	Little oxygen, hard to breathe, hard to think Wind and snowstorms can be deadly

Step 4. Use the chart to write a summary of what you learned.

Writing a summary helps you keep what you've read in your head. Summarizing can also help you identify the most important points of your reading.

Summary

Mountain climbing is a difficult and dangerous sport. A group of moviemakers went to Mount Everest to make an IMAX film, and they learned firsthand how dangerous climbing is.

Here's how the student began her summary. Use this beginning as a model to write your own summary of the article on mountain climbing.
Your Summary:

____

____

____

____

____

Apply It............ Try using KWL Plus on a reading assignment you have. First preview the assignment to get an idea of the topic. Then draw a KWL chart. Fill in the K section with things you know about the topic. Then fill in the W section with things you want to know about it. After you have finished reading, fill in the L section with information you have learned. Finally, write a summary of your reading.

Strategy 2 Outlining

Understand It...... Writing an outline can be a great way to create a study guide. When you take notes using an outline, you first preview to find the topic. You think of what you know about the topic, then you read. When you have finished reading, you review by making an outline. Use your outline to write a summary of the main points.

Try It.............. Read the article about the writer Sir Arthur Conan Doyle. He created a character you've probably heard of—Sherlock Holmes. Follow along with the student who has read the article and is creating an outline.

Step 1. Preview the selection.

Look at the title, the photograph, and the subheadings. Get an idea of the points the author is making. How is the article organized? You've probably read a few biographies either in school or on your own. You've seen that biographies can be organized in several ways. That is what the student thought as he skimmed the biography in this lesson.

The author could have written this biography in many ways. It could have been written chronologically—from Doyle's birth to his death. It could focus on one part of his life, such as the books he wrote. It could also show the events or people that shaped Doyle or his work. I can imagine other possibilities too. Which organization is this? The subheadings might tell me.

Below, write what you can tell about the way the author organized the biography from previewing the article.

____

____

____

____

Step 2. Read, then make an outline.

When most people make an outline, they use a formal style that may be familiar to you. It begins with Roman numerals for major ideas. Capital letters are used for major points that are part of each major idea. Numbers are used for supporting evidence for each major point. Titles and subheadings can help you find the major points and ideas in a piece of writing.

Here is how the student began outlining the article on the next two pages. After you read, add to the outline form to create a complete outline of the biography of Sir Arthur Conan Doyle.

Sir Arthur Conan Doyle

I. Early life
   A. From large family
   B. Studied to become a doctor
      1. met Dr. Joseph Bell
      2. learned to make deductions about patients
   C. Began to write novels
II. A Fork in the Road
   A. ______
      1. ______
      2. ______
   B. ______
      1. ______
      2. ______
III. The Later Years
   A. ______
      1. ______
      2. ______
   B. ______
      1. ______
      2. ______
   C. ______

Sir Arthur Conan Doyle

Almost everyone knows the image. The thin man bent over a footprint is peering through a magnifying glass. Who else but Sherlock Holmes could be examining that footprint? Who else could solve the crime? The man who created Holmes was as interesting as his fictional character. Sir Arthur Conan Doyle lived a life of wide interests and great passions.

Early Life

Doyle was one of ten children. This was a large family even in the 1800s. Supporting so many children was a struggle. Doyle's uncles helped the family by sending Arthur to a Jesuit school. Although Doyle was a good student, he was unhappy.

Strategy Tip

Sometimes a new subheading signals that the author is introducing a new major idea.

Sherlock Holmes and Watson

Doyle went on to medical school. There he met a professor who made a big impact on his life. The professor, Dr. Joseph Bell, was known for his ability to make deductions about his patients. Doyle later put that skill to use in his writing. He had Sherlock Holmes make deductions about his cases.

After graduation, Doyle served as a ship's doctor. He then entered practice with Dr. George Budd. Their partnership was not a happy one. In his spare time, Doyle did work he liked: writing. In 1887 his first work featuring Sherlock Holmes appeared. It was called *A Study in Scarlet.* During his time with Budd, Doyle kept writing. He published a long historical novel and then the Holmes mystery *The Sign of the Four.* In those years, Doyle's interests grew. He married Louise ("Touie") Hawkins in 1885. The next year he began to develop an interest in psychic phenomena. He would remain interested in this topic all of his life.

A Fork in the Road

In 1890, Doyle needed a change. He went back to medical school to become an eye doctor. Because Doyle had few patients, he used his spare time to write. The Sherlock Holmes books remained popular. Holmes appeared in four novels and 56 stories. In 1893, Doyle grew tired of his creation. He killed off Holmes in a story titled "The Final Problem." There was a public outcry, but Doyle was unmoved. Then in 1905, he brought the detective back to life in *The Return of Sherlock Holmes.*

In the meantime, Doyle was ready for new adventures. He and his wife traveled to Cairo, Egypt. When a war started there, Doyle began a career as a war reporter.

The Later Years

When his wife died in 1906, Doyle became depressed. The following year, he married Jean Leckie, who had been a friend for years. Doyle then developed another character, Professor Challenger. In his time, Challenger became almost as famous as Holmes. When World War I broke out, Doyle formed a volunteer force. He also served as a war journalist.

After his son's death in the war, Doyle turned to a topic that had long interested him: **spiritualism**. During the rest of his life, Doyle tried to prove that mediums could reach the dead. He also studied other **spiritualist** topics. In 1930, Doyle died of a heart attack.

Doyle's colorful life displays his energy and wide-ranging interests. His reputation today, though, rests on his fictional detective, Sherlock Holmes. The detective that Doyle tried to kill lives on and keeps Doyle's memory alive, too.

Vocabulary Tip

Do you know the meaning of *spiritualism* or *spiritualist*? Think about the meaning of the word *spirit.* That will help you figure out the meanings of both new words.

Strategy Tip

When you are looking back at your outline, underline a few words or phrases that seem especially important. Underlining will help you remember these points.

Step 3. Summarize what you have learned.

Look over your outline. Does it show you how the biography is organized and what the important points are? Add to your outline if you need to. Then use it to help you write a summary of the biography of Arthur Conan Doyle. Here is how the student began his summary of the biography:

> Summary
>
> Sir Arthur Conan Doyle was famous for his writing about Sherlock Holmes, but he did many other things in his life too. His family was large and poor, but Doyle was able to go to medical school to become a doctor.
>
> Then, though . . .

Now write your own summary of the biography on the lines below. Be sure to use your outline as you write to remind you of the major points and the evidence that supports them.

____

____

____

____

____

____

____

____

Apply It........... Try outlining a reading assignment you have. First preview the assignment to see what the topic is. Notice the headings and subheadings. They will help you create your outline. Then draw the outline form on a separate piece of paper. Read the assignment, then create your outline. Remember to note the most important ideas on the Roman numeral lines.

When your outline is complete, use it to write a paragraph that summarizes your reading.

Strategy 3 PACA

Understand It..... Active readers often use a reading strategy called PACA. PACA stands for **P**redicting **A**nd **C**onfirming **A**ctivity. The strategy is based on the idea that a reader can often predict what a selection will be about. After you make a prediction, look for information that confirms you are right—or wrong. What you find out can help you understand your reading.

PACA is a good strategy to use when you know enough about what you are reading to make a prediction about it. When you predict and then check your prediction, you become an active reader. Active readers get more out of reading because they think about what they read.

Try It.............. The following selection shows a debate about school uniforms. Maybe you have an opinion on the issue. Because you have heard about the topic, the PACA strategy is a good one to use. Think about what you already know about school uniforms. You may be able to predict what people on both sides of the debate might think. Try the PACA method with this student.

Step 1. Predict what you will read.

When you predict, you preview the writing to see what it is about. The student looked at the titles of these essays. They told her the selection was a debate about whether students should wear uniforms to school. She thought about what she already knew about the debate over uniforms.

We don't have school uniforms, but I know some kids who wear them to school. What do they think about them? Do they mind wearing them? What would wearing a uniform be like? How would I feel? Maybe I'd like not having to think about what to put on every morning. Maybe I'd hate the way a uniform looked.

The student then looked quickly at the writing. She wrote a prediction about what the reasons for and against school uniforms might be. Here is the beginning of her PACA chart. Add your own predictions to the chart.

Predictions	Support
the person who is against school uniforms will write that wearing uniforms will cost more	

Step 2. Read and confirm your predictions.

Strategy Tip
As you write your predictions, leave plenty of space to write points you did not think of and to make notes later.

Keep your predictions close at hand when you read. First, when you see information that confirms one prediction, make a check mark next to it. Second, when you find points in the writing you did not predict, write them and draw a star next to each one. Finally, cross out predictions that are wrong to avoid confusion.

After she began reading, the student began marking and revising her list of predictions. Remember that you wrote predictions too. If they turn out to be wrong, change them.

Predictions		Support
the person who is against school uniforms will write that wearing uniforms will cost more	✓	
students should be able to make choices	*	

Debate: Should Schools Require Uniforms?

Against Uniforms: By Kate Monahan

When I think of having to wear uniforms to school, my heart just sinks. It's bad enough with all the rules we have to follow. I wouldn't be surprised if lots of people dropped out.

There are many reasons making students wear uniforms is a terrible idea. For one, it would end up costing more. Even if you had uniforms to wear to school, you would still need clothes for the rest of the time. You'd need two sets of clothes, and that gets expensive.

Should students really be able to choose?

Some people say that violence would stop if we wore uniforms. I think that's stupid. If people are going to fight, they're going to fight. What people are wearing isn't going to stop them from fighting. They'll just find another reason.

It's the same with people who say that unpopular kids can't keep up and uniforms will make everyone equal. That doesn't matter. If someone is cool, he won't get picked on, even if his clothes aren't the best. But if someone is not cool, the best clothes on the planet will not keep him from being made fun of. Making us wear certain types of clothes won't make any difference.

What I'd really like to know is what happened to the First Amendment to the Constitution. Doesn't that say everyone has freedom of speech? Well, my freedom of speech is in how I dress. This is a **constitutional** wrong! I have a right to express myself. Clothes are how I do that.

Vocabulary Tip

If you know the word *constitution*, you can figure out the meaning of the word *constitutional*, an adjective based on *constitution*.

I thought school was supposed to teach students how to make choices. Making us wear uniforms says that adults think we can't make good choices. It says that adults don't want to give us the chance to *learn* how to make good choices. Forcing us to wear uniforms also shows that adults don't trust us.

I don't want to go to a school that forces everyone to be the same. I think it will create boring people who don't question anything and who blindly accept anything they are told. It is my civil right to wear what I want!

For Uniforms: By Edie Hamilton

As a student who would have to wear uniforms if the school board votes for them, I think I have a right to speak. There are several reasons I think having school uniforms is a great idea.

Don't uniforms mean a kind of equality?

First, parents and students spend way too much money on school clothes. Everyone has to have the latest shoes, the latest jeans, the latest whatever, and that means lots of money. Not everyone has that kind of money. If we had uniforms, no one would be able to look down on someone because she didn't have the right clothes.

I also think that if we wore uniforms, there would be less gang violence. Right now, everyone is on edge. We never know when someone is going to wear clothes that will end up with people fighting over gang colors. Even though the school tries to stop it, teachers don't always know what different kinds of clothing mean.

I think if everyone wore uniforms, people would think of school more seriously. It would be like a job, not a social place. You would know that when you put on your uniform, it was time to think about school.

I know some people think choosing what to wear to school is a matter of self-expression. To those people, I say, "Get a life!" It's what's inside that counts. You can express yourself by how you act. Most important, you can express yourself by what you produce in school.

If we had uniforms, I think we'd be much better off. We would have to spend less money on clothes. There wouldn't be as much violence. People would be able to focus on what's really important: learning.

Step 3. Support your predictions.

Look at what you wrote in your chart. Make notes by each point to make sure it sticks in your mind. Maybe you'll find supporting arguments for the points you wrote and for the main points the debaters made. Write this evidence in the Support column of your chart.

Here is how the student began adding to her predictions.

Predictions		Support
the person who is against school uniforms will write that wearing uniforms will cost more	✓	uniforms are expensive need clothes for home as well as school
students should be able to make choices	*	uniforms suggest that adults don't think students can make good choices

Apply It............ Use the PACA strategy with a reading assignment you have. Look it over. What do the headings tell you about the topic? What do you already know about it? Write your predictions in your own PACA chart.

Then read the assignment, looking for information about your predictions. When you see information that confirms a prediction, make a check mark next to it. When you see points you did not predict, write them and put a star in front of each one. Cross out predictions that are wrong. Finally, write in the evidence or examples that support each point. You should now have a good review of the important points in your reading assignment.

Strategy 4 PLAN

Understand It...... PLAN works well for people who learn best when they can make a picture of what they are learning. PLAN stands for **P**redict, **L**ocate, **A**dd, and **N**ote. When you use PLAN, you create a word map that predicts what you will read.

There are many ways to draw word maps. If all the information in a reading relates to one subject, you might draw a wheel with spokes.

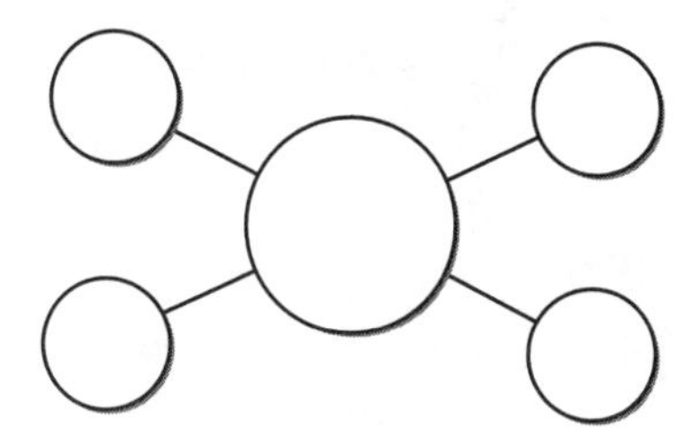

If an article compares and contrasts several different things, a Venn diagram might work best. Write the ideas the subjects have in common in the space that links both circles. Write the information that is true of only one subject in the outside of one circle.

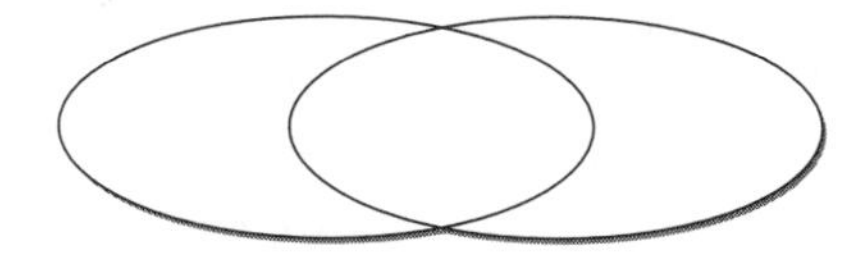

If an article is organized by time, you can create a sequence chart. In a sequence chart, you write events in the order in which they happen. Arrows connect the boxes.

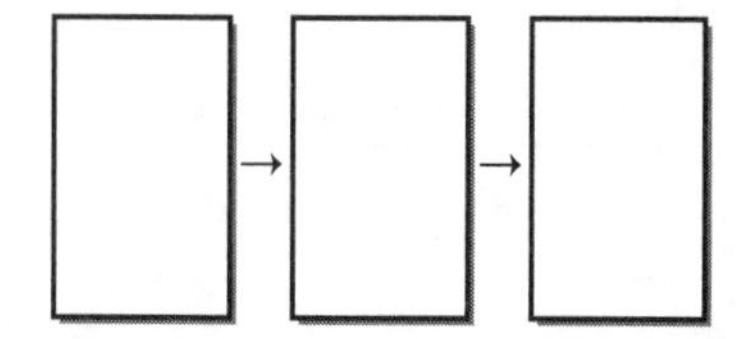

Maybe you know another way to show how a piece of writing is organized. Feel free to draw any kind of word map that helps you organize the information you're learning.

Try It.............. Once you choose a graphic, you locate and add information to it that tells you whether your ideas were right. Then you fill in the map with that information. Finally, you note your understanding of what you read.

On pages 18–19 is an article about Koko, a gorilla who learned sign language. To help her understand the article, a student used PLAN as she read. Read along to see how to use PLAN.

Step 1. Predict what you will learn.

When the student first looked at the article, she didn't see any subheadings. She previewed the paragraphs to see what the article was about. She noticed that the article did not compare two things. This told her that she couldn't use a Venn diagram.

Then she noticed that the article was not written in time order, so she decided not to use a sequence chart. Finally, she decided that everything in the article was about one subject—a gorilla named Koko—so she started a wheel-and-spoke diagram. She put Koko's name in the middle. Then she arranged around it information she knew about Koko.

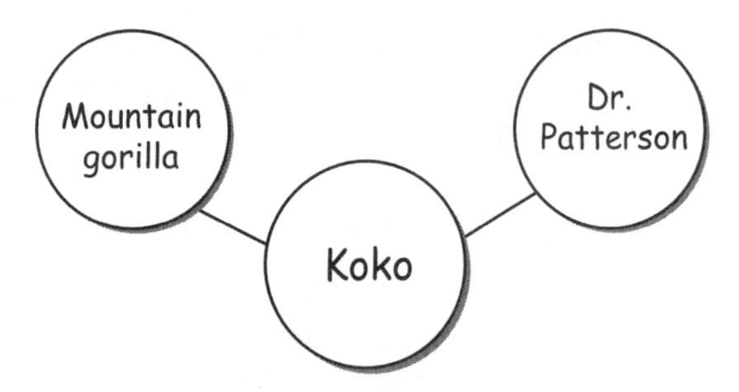

Now preview the selection and make your own predictions about what will be in the article. Use the diagram below to begin using the PLAN strategy. Write the topic—Koko—in the middle circle. Write the main points you think the article will contain in the connecting circles. Add circles as you need them to fit other points.

Strategy Tip

Leave enough space in your diagram so you can add more circles. These circles will contain other main points you find and information about each point.

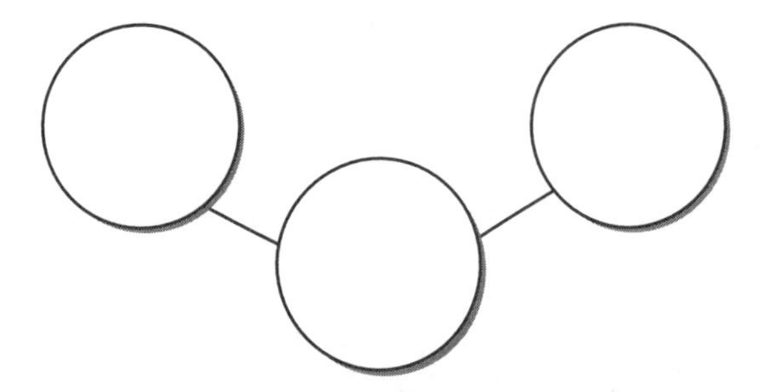

Step 2. Locate information you will look for as you read.

Look at your diagram. Put check marks next to ideas or people you know something about. Put a question mark next to anything unfamiliar to you. Marking your diagram will help you think about what you already know about the subject and will prepare you to understand what you will read. Here's what the student thought as she created her diagram:

I think I've heard of Koko, so I'll put a check mark there. I also know something about mountain gorillas, so I'll check that. I've never heard of Dr. Patterson, so I'll write a question mark by her name.

The student's wheel-and-spoke diagram now looked like this:

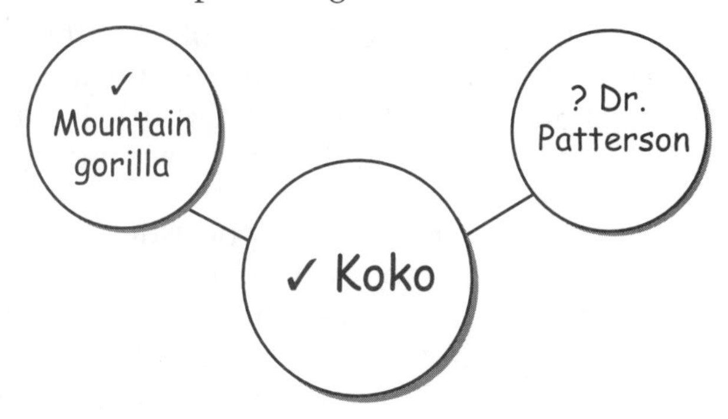

Locate ideas or people you know something about on your diagram. Place check marks there. Put question marks in front of ideas or people you know nothing about.

Step 3. Read, then add information to your map.

Read the selection about Koko. Then write words or short phrases that remind you of the supporting facts or details under each main point. If you missed major points, add them to the diagram, along with details that support them.

Here's how the student began filling in her diagram:

✓
Mountain gorilla
like us: fingers, toes, etc.
huge—500 pounds,
complex social structure

? Dr. Patterson

✓ Koko

? Koko's pet

Strategy Tip

Don't copy the article on your diagram. Use key words or short phrases that remind you only of the main points.

After you read, fill in your own diagram. Add major points and write words that will remind you of evidence or details for each point.

Vocabulary Tip

Even if you don't know the word *genetic,* you might have heard the word *gene.* Genes are the building blocks of cells that make us who we are. *Genetic* is a word that describes something related to genes.

Koko, the Talking Gorilla

We all know that animals can communicate. A cat's purr can tell us it loves being petted. Dogs mope when they have done something wrong. However, a gorilla is different. When a mountain gorilla named Koko began understanding human language and reacting to it, people took note.

Gorillas and humans belong to the same **genetic** family. Gorillas have arms and legs, as we do. They also have ten fingers and ten toes. They have

Koko and Dr. Patterson

32 teeth. Their faces look a little like ours. They are much bigger than we are, though. A full-grown male can be taller than 6 feet and weigh about 500 pounds. In the wild, gorillas care for their young and play with one another. They have a complex social structure that's similar in many ways to ours.

In 1972, Dr. Penny Patterson was a graduate student at Stanford University. She saw Koko at the San Francisco Zoo, where she was doing a study. Koko had been sick, and she wasn't living with the other gorillas. The zoo officials were afraid she would die without special care.

At about that time, Patterson went to a talk about a chimpanzee that had learned 132 words in sign language. Patterson decided to find out whether a gorilla could learn sign language. She also wanted to help Koko. Within weeks, Patterson had taught Koko a few words in American Sign Language (ASL). People who use ASL make hand motions instead of saying words. Koko was the first gorilla to learn a human language.

Strategy Tip

Some readers find that using different-colored highlighters can help them remember what they read. They highlight the main points in one color and the supporting details in another color. This step can help you remember what you read.

Patterson began her study 25 years ago. Since then, Koko has learned 800 signs and 2,000 English words. One year, she told Patterson she wanted a cat for her birthday. Patterson gave her a toy cat. Koko responded by signing, "That red." To Koko, the word red means "angry." Koko didn't want a toy. She wanted a real cat.

Finally, she got one. Patterson's assistant brought three kittens to the lab. Koko played with one. She signed, "Cat do scratch. Koko love." Koko cared for the cat. She played with her. When the cat died after being hit by a car, Koko cried.

In 1976, Patterson began the Gorilla Foundation. The foundation helps save the habitat of the mountain gorilla. Today, about 600 mountain gorillas still live in the wild. The members also work to save other animals that live in the African rain forest.

Step 4. Note what you have learned.

Now review your diagram. If it does not show how the article is organized, you may want to redo it. Close your eyes and review the important points or write a summary. Then redraw your diagram. In addition to checking your understanding of your reading, you can use your diagram as a study guide. The notes you made will help you review for tests.

Apply It............

Use the PLAN strategy with a reading assignment you have. Preview the reading, looking for the way the information is organized. If there is one main topic, make a wheel-and-spoke diagram. If your assignment compares two people or ideas, use a Venn diagram. If the assignment tells events in time order, try a sequence chart. Then read and revise your drawing if necessary. As a last step, make notes about what you've learned to help you remember the main points of the reading.

Strategy Tip

Try different strategies to help you remember what you read. Use the method that works best for you.

Unit 2
Reading in Language Arts

Language arts includes many types of reading. It includes short stories, novels, plays, articles, and movie reviews. Most of the reading you do for fun is probably language arts reading. In school, you may do other kinds of language arts reading, including biographies and essays. Often in language arts reading, you are learning skills such as how to write a letter or how to use punctuation.

How Language Arts Reading Is Organized

Even though there are many different kinds of readings in language arts, there are a few basic ways those readings are organized. When you preview, you can often learn what kind of organization a writer has chosen. If you can recognize the organization, you will understand a reading more easily because you will know what to expect. Here are a few of the common patterns you may see in language arts readings.

Main Idea and Details. This is probably the most common way of organizing language arts reading. In this pattern, everything in the article is connected to one topic or main idea. In a grammar book, the topic may be prepositions. In a magazine article, the topic may be the Olympics. When you see this pattern, you know that there will be several main points that are connected to the topic. These main points will explain the topic. Below is a drawing of how an article with one main point is organized.

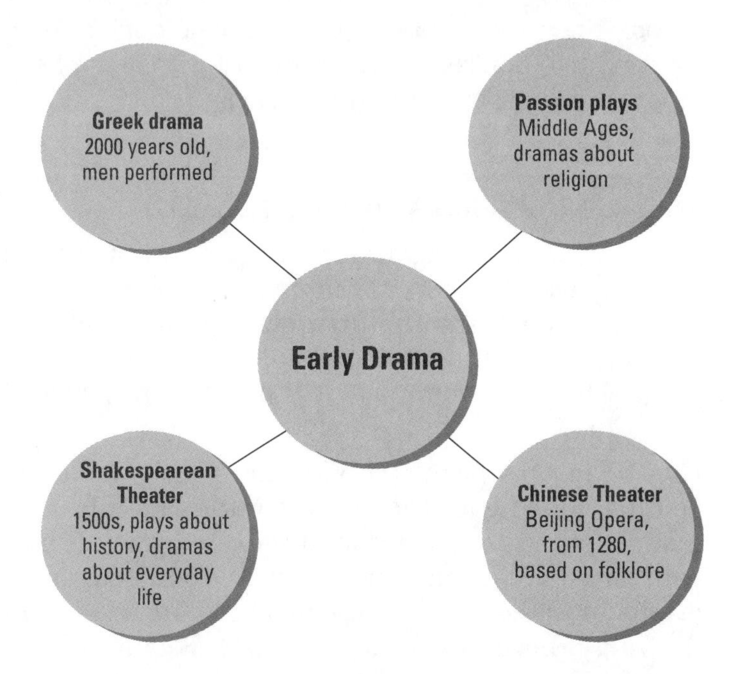

Compare and Contrast. You will find this kind of organization when a writer is showing the similarities and differences between two or more ideas. For example, a review may include the differences and similarities between two TV shows. Below is a drawing of how an article that compares and contrasts two ideas might be organized.

Batman and Robin Again

Different	Same	Different
The TV Show Many episodes, with weak plots, no special effects, poor writing	Based on cartoon strip, with costumes, unlikely plots	The Movies Few movies, with great special effects, big stars

Sequence of Events. This type of organization is common in diaries, true-life adventure stories, and biographies. It is easy to recognize. When you preview, you'll notice that the dates follow one another in order. Often, with a reading such as a diary, you know the sections are in time order. Below is a drawing of how an article that lists events in time order might be organized.

Settler's Timeline

Oct. 13, 1850	Dec. 14, 1850	June 20, 1851	Dec. 25, 1851
Settler comes to the frontier	Shanty house finished	First crop in	First Christmas in new house

Getting the Most from Your Reading

If you can recognize the way a reading is organized, you will be better able to understand what you read. You will be able to think about what kind of information might be next and how all the points in the reading fit together. Making drawings like the ones on these two pages can show you these patterns. Thinking about how a reading is organized can help you understand—and remember—what you read.

Lesson 1 Diary: When the Rains Wouldn't Come

Understand It...... This selection is about something you might have heard of—the Dust Bowl. PACA is a good strategy to use when you know something about the topic and can make guesses about other information. Look at the headings and the photograph for hints about what you will learn in this selection.

Hint
You can review the PACA strategy on page 12.

Try It............... Think about the words *Dust Bowl.* You probably know something about that time in United States history. Use what you know to help you make predictions as you preview the diary. Below is a drawing of a PACA chart. Draw your own chart on a separate sheet of paper. Read the diary once. Write your predictions in the Predictions column of your chart. As you read again, check the points you predicted in the first column. Write in points you did not predict. Write the evidence that supports your predictions in the Support column.

Predictions	Support

When the Rains Wouldn't Come

June 7, 1934 Sometimes it feels like we eat and drink dust. It's never far from our thoughts. Ma said today that she doesn't need a broom—she needs a shovel. She sounded really mad, but then Pa came in from the fields, and she put her head on his shoulder and cried.

June 21, 1934 Every day it looks like it's going to rain. The rain clouds join overhead, and they look like water, all heavy and black. But then, by late afternoon, they're gone and we're left again without rain. I saw Pa looking at the sky, and his shoulders slumped. Then he tried to cheer me up—"Don't worry, Scout, it'll rain." For some reason, that made me feel worse. His voice just didn't sound real. We both know if nothing changes, we'll have to leave.

June 22, 1934 I heard Ma and Pa talking. She was saying, "If we just hang on long enough, it'll change, John. It has to. Is all our work for nothing?" He just shook his head and shrugged his shoulders and then sat in the chair. "If it doesn't change soon, Margaret, we'll have no choice."

July 30, 1934 How can it possibly be—how can it go so long without rain? The dust blows into huge drifts that look almost like snow. People are leaving. I saw the Campbells go yesterday, everything packed up in their car. They sold out a couple of weeks ago, got just about nothing for all their stuff, Ma said. She said, under her breath, that it was giving up—but who could blame them? I wonder if we'll be leaving too.

August 14, 1934 Ma and Pa have been talking to each other in low voices for about five days now. When I come into the room, they stop. I know we're leaving.

August 15, 1934 Sure enough, when I came down for breakfast, Ma and Pa sat Jordy and me down and told us, in these too-cheery voices, that we'll be starting a new life in California. They pulled out magazine pictures they had of the orange trees and the ocean, and they told us that's where we'll be going. Jordy said, in his anxious voice, "Can Peanut go?" Pa stopped a moment and then said, really gently, "Jordy, we won't have any room for a dog." So Jordy stormed out, crying his eyes out.

Strategy Tip

What does the photograph show you about the Dust Bowl? Add this information to the Predictions column of your PACA chart.

Look at the people. Look at the house. What do they tell you about the amount of dust there is?

August 19, 1934 It didn't take long, once they had made up their minds. It's nothing to them, I guess, to leave a place we've lived our whole lives. They don't care. We sold everything—the one cow we had left, the farm equipment. Nobody wanted most of the stuff in our house, so we left it. It was strange, just seeing those things sitting there, like they are waiting for us to come back. Jordy's not speaking to Ma and Pa because Peanut isn't going. Pa is out there now, finishing the packing. Ma couldn't bear to part with her good dishes, so Pa **strapped** them on the top of the car in a special box. We're leaving first thing tomorrow.

Vocabulary Tip

If you know that a *strap* is a "piece of flexible material used to hold something down," you can figure out that the verb *strapped* means "to hold something with a strap."

August 20, 1934 I looked back at the house and the farm as long as I could. Maybe Oklahoma wasn't the best place ever, but it is home. It was strange, leaving. Nobody came to see us off. Most of our friends are gone already. The ones that are left seem too beaten down to do much of anything. Maybe it will be wonderful in California, with the ocean and the orange trees. I keep that thought in my mind.

August 25, 1934 We don't have much money, so we camp along the way and buy a little food at a time. I hear Ma and Pa talking about money all the time. They're afraid we won't have enough money to get us to California.

August 31, 1934 All along the way we've been seeing people who look just like us. They have everything they own on their cars or in their trucks. They're all headed for California. How could there be enough work for everybody? I also found out that all of us travelers have a bad name. People call us "Okies" because we're from Oklahoma. The way they say it, though—they spit it out like it's a bad word and we're bad people. I saw Ma flinch when we went to a service station to ask for water and the man there swore at her and called her an Okie.

September 1, 1934 We've been playing a game—what will life be like in California? Ma imagines the smell of flowers and fruit everywhere and the breeze from the ocean. I think of rain and green and a big white house with a grass yard. Pa talks about working and saving enough to buy a farm there, a farm where tomatoes grow as big as his fist. Jordy talks about going back home and getting Peanut so he can live with us.

September 3, 1934 We're in California. It's not so great. There are people just like us everywhere, camped in ugly yards of dirt. When Pa asks where to go to get work, they look at him like he's crazy. "Don't you think we'd have work if we knew?" one man said to him, glaring. Now I'm scared. What if there isn't any work here, either? What will we do? How will we live?

After you finish reading, go back and find the evidence that supports each prediction you made. Write this information in the Support column. Use the chart to review what you learned.

Apply It............ To check your understanding of the diary entries, circle the best answer to each of the following questions.

Test Tip

Look closely at the wording of questions. The word *incorrect* in question 1 tells you that three of the answers are correct, or true, according to the diary.

1. Which of the following is *incorrect*?
   a. The family swore never to leave Oklahoma.
   b. Every day it looks like rain, but the rain doesn't come.
   c. People use the word *Okie* as an insult.
   d. The family travels from Oklahoma to California.

2. You could describe the narrator as
   a. a worried child.
   b. a lonely child.
   c. a family pet.
   d. an unhappy parent.

3. In the August 31 entry, the word *flinch* means
   a. to spit.
   b. to say a swear word.
   c. to make a quick movement backward.
   d. to insult someone.

4. The travelers from Oklahoma probably have a bad reputation because
   a. they are considered bad luck.
   b. there are many of them and they are poor.
   c. they are lazy.
   d. they make traffic on the roads.

5. The diary writer's mood when the family first decides to leave could best be described as
   a. happy.
   b. accepting.
   c. furious.
   d. unconcerned.

Use the lines below to write your answers for numbers 6 and 7. Use your PACA chart to help you.

6. Write a summary of the important events that occur in these entries.

____

____

____

____

____

7. Imagine that you are the diary writer. Do you think you would feel the same? Would you feel differently? Explain your answer.

____

____

____

____

____

Lesson 2 True Adventure: The Underwater World of the Moles

Understand It.....

Hint
You can review the PLAN strategy on page 16.

This selection is a true-life adventure story about cave diving. Consider using the PLAN strategy with this reading. First, preview the story to see how it is organized. Is there one main topic? Does the story compare two people or ideas? Is the information presented in time order? Skimming will also help you find out a little about the topic. Once you know how the story is organized you can choose the graphic you think best fits it.

Try It..............

Below you'll find three possible PLAN graphics. You can use one of them or create a graphic of your own. Remember to make your graphic large enough so you can add notes. Predict what the main points will be. Write them in the graphic. Write check marks next to things you know about. Write question marks next to things you don't know about.

Then read the story. As you read a second time, locate important information. Write in information that supports the main points. If you missed main points, add them to your graphic.

Strategy Tip
Sketch different graphics as you preview the story. You may find that the second or third one fits the story better than the first one you try.

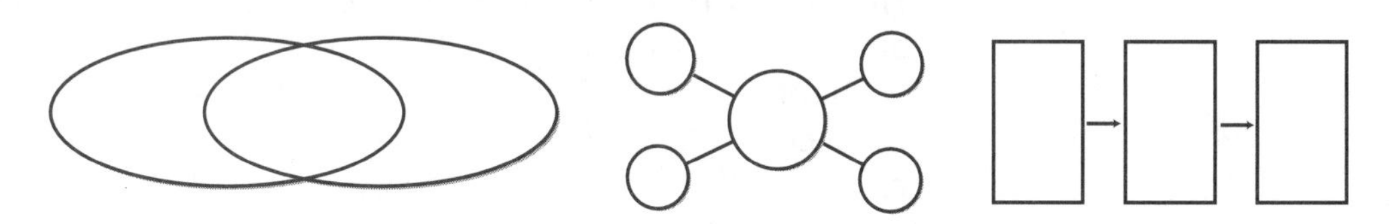

The Underwater World of the Moles

Cave diving sounds frightening to many people: being underwater and trapped in a tiny cave at the same time. For some adventurers, though, cave diving is the best thrill they know. Every cave diver imagines discovering an underwater cave no one else has explored.

A group of Florida cave divers gave themselves the name "the Moles." They specialize in learning the secrets of the limestone cave system under north central Florida. It is the largest underwater river system in the United States. The Moles know that underwater system better than anyone. For years, they have explored it and mapped it. Nothing excites them more than discovering a new way into the system.

What does it take to be a Mole? Certainly, a love of exploration is important. Scuba diving skills are crucial. Having very little fear helps. A Mole must be able to squeeze into tight spaces without feeling anxious.

On this night, the Moles stand on the edge of a water hole. In its dark depths might lurk snakes, alligators—who knows? That's the point—the Moles want to know. One puts on a wet suit with a hood and fins and a crash helmet with a **miner's light**. He attaches a tank of air. He carries an exploration line. One end is tied to a tree on shore.

Vocabulary Tip
When you see an unfamiliar phrase, study the words in the phrase. A *miner's light* is strapped to a helmet. Think about what a miner does and why a miner might need a light. This will help you understand what a *miner's light* is.

The Mole slips into the murky water. Soon the bubbles disappear. That means the Mole has found the entrance to a cave. Kicking at the wrong moment can stir up a cloud of silt, which means a diver can't see an inch in front of his face. A diver can get lost. Make a couple of turns in an underwater cave, and it is easy to become so disoriented you never come out again.

Air is another issue. A diver can only carry so much. One heartbreaking story told in cave-diving circles is of Bill Hurst. He was an experienced diver who, in 1976, took a wrong turn. When he realized he didn't have enough air to get back, he spent his last moments writing good-bye to his family.

The Mole is still underwater. Despite the frightening possibilities, the other Moles on the shore aren't worried. They're sure the diver in the water has found an unexplored cave, the prize Moles live for.

Suddenly, the Mole bursts through the surface. He strips off his mask and grins. There *is* a cave, and it flows into the limestone cave system. The Mole followed the cave down 40 feet before it became too narrow.

That information is all it takes—the other Moles strap on their equipment. One by one, they splash in and follow their friend's line down to the hole. When they come back up, they're dizzy with discovery. One reports that he was pushing through a passage when what he thought was a diver in a black wet suit swam toward him. When the swimmer ran into his headlamp, the Mole realized it was no diver. It was a 6-foot alligator that, the Mole reports, was as surprised and alarmed as he was.

After the dive, the Moles settle down to the business of mapping what they've discovered. They've found another piece of the puzzle, the intricate maze that those who inhabit north central Florida unknowingly live on top of. Underneath is the world of the Moles, a mysterious, secret world that few know about—and even fewer want to enter.

When you finish reading, look at your graphic. Does it contain the important information from the story as well as the supporting points? To make sure you understand what you read, make notes. You can do that with a summary, an oral review, or a list. Use the review process that works best for you.

Apply It. . . . . To check your understanding of the story, circle the best answer to each of the following questions.

1. From this adventure story, you learn that a Mole is
   a. a name for a large underwater cave system.
   b. a name for the Florida Coast Guard.
   c. a name given to diving teachers.
   d. a name of a group of cave divers.

Test Tip

Question 2 asks you for the *main* idea of the article. The other answers may have been mentioned, but there is only one *main* idea.

Test Tip

Two of the answers to question 4 say almost the same thing. Before you choose an answer, think carefully about all four choices and how they apply to the story.

2. The main idea of this story is that
   a. cave diving is dangerous.
   b. Florida is a great place for cave divers.
   c. the Moles dive in caves for the thrill of discovery.
   d. cave diving is the most frightening sport known.

3. In this story, the word *disoriented* means
   a. losing the sense of location.
   b. running out of air.
   c. panicking.
   d. being lost.

4. The author tells the story of Bill Hurst to show
   a. how calm cave divers are.
   b. how brave cave divers are.
   c. that even experienced cave divers can get into trouble.
   d. how important it is to have enough air with you when you dive.

5. Two of the dangers of cave diving that the author mentions are
   a. swallowing too much water and becoming disoriented.
   b. being lost in a cloud of silt and having an air tank that is too large.
   c. forgetting to use the line and getting lost in a cloud of silt.
   d. becoming disoriented and kicking up silt.

Use the lines below to write your answers for numbers 6 and 7. Use your PLAN chart to help you.

6. Describe the steps a Mole takes while exploring a new underwater cave.

____

____

____

____

7. What do you think the most exciting thing about being a cave diver would be? What would be the most frightening thing? Support your answer with facts from the story.

____

____

____

____

Lesson 3 Magazine Article: The Nutty Invention Files

Understand It...... From reading the title, you probably have a good idea of what this article is about—nutty inventions. You might not have heard of the inventions themselves though. PLAN might be a good strategy for understanding this article. You can preview the article and get a good idea of its organization. Then you can use that structure to help you understand the article.

Hint
You can review the PLAN strategy on page 16.

Try It.............. When you use the PLAN strategy, you first preview the article. Is there one main topic? Are two people or ideas being compared? Is the information presented in time order? Remember to predict what will be in the article and use this information in your graphic. Next, locate information that you know something about and add check marks next to it. Add question marks next to ideas you don't know about. As you read, write words that give you evidence or details for each point. Finally, note what you learned to help you review. Below are drawings of the three different graphics you can use to help you organize what you learn.

Strategy Tip
You might want to draw a wheel with spokes for this article. Write the word *inventions* in the center. Then connect the examples of inventions to the word *inventions* with spokes.

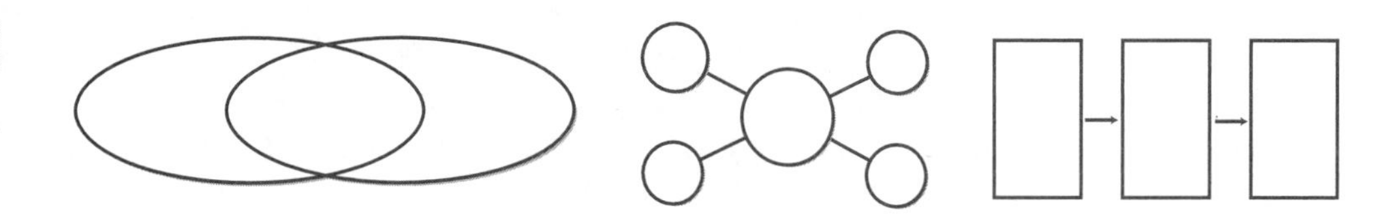

The Nutty Invention Files

Some very strange ideas are buried in the patent office. Since 1790, when President George Washington signed the first national patent law, inventors have been showing up at the patent office with ideas. Some are good; some are not so good. Some, it must be said, are truly amazing. Here are some unusual inventions that you might not have heard of.

Tail Lights for Horses
Lugging humans around on its back might make a horse embarrassed enough. In 1937, John E. Torbert, Jr., made life worse for horses. He claimed his invention would "afford amusement to observers." More important, it would keep cars from running into horses. The device was designed to be attached to a horse's tail. It has safety reflectors. A shield protects against wind. The swinging of the horse's tail turns on a wiper that cleans the glass on the shield. The inventor adds that the device can also be attached to a dog. No dog we know would wear it, however.

Magazine Article: The Nutty Invention Files

Vocabulary Tip

Aeroplane is an alternate spelling for *airplane.* Since the word was used in 1915, its spelling was different from today's.

The "Good Luck" Life-Saving Device

In 1915, Michael Kispeter patented his Life-Saving Apparatus. It is designed to save "a person dropping from an **aeroplane** or airship over land or over water." Kispeter's invention is based on a life jacket. It is lined with cushions that inflate. A spring helmet is attached to the jacket, and a parachute fastens to the body over the jacket. Kispeter's drawing shows a man with his arms outstretched. He looks as if he doesn't care if his life is short.

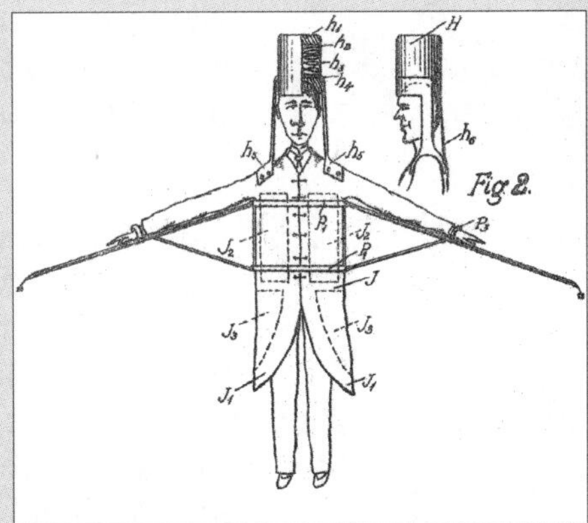

Kispeter's Life-Saving Apparatus

It Grates! It Slices! It Catches Mice!

In 1897, Robert Gardiner decided the world desperately needed a cheese grater that could also catch mice. So he invented one. Gardiner's box is shaped like a cylinder. It is made of sheet metal and has several removable lids. As Gardiner writes in his application, changing lids makes the box "useful for other purposes (after the first contents are removed.)" What other purposes could you invent for this device?

Holding Tank for Bank Robbers

Bank robbers and gangsters were busy in the 1920s. Have you heard of the famous gangster Al Capone? People all over the country must have been afraid of gangsters. There is no other way to explain this invention. In 1921, Stanley Valinski invented the "man-catching tank." He tells us, though, that the device has two jobs. It's not just a man-catcher. It's also a man-holder. The tank is kept in an out-of-the way place in a bank. Inside, the watchman peers through the peep holes, looking for robbers. When he spots one, he drives the man-catching tank over to the bank robber. Then he puts the bank robber inside. Valinski is not quite clear about the details, however. Does the robber just hang around, waiting for the tank to reach him, and then politely step inside?

Jerky Is the Word

Just to prove that nutty ideas don't only come from decades ago, we offer egg jerky. It was invented in 1985. Until then, the inventors tell us, jerky was made from meat. Egg jerky is based on the discovery that eggs make a perfectly lovely jerky. First the eggs are beaten. Then seasonings and soy are added, and the mixture is formed into sheets. The sheets are dried and dried again—and again. However, they are not, we suspect, eaten by anyone.

Warm Breath, Warm Feet

Animal heat is the clue here, according to the inventor. William Steiger's "Improvement in Foot-Warmers" (1877) may be clunky. However, if it keeps your feet warm, who cares? Steiger tells us (1) our lungs are the source of animal heat, (2) our feet are too far from our lungs, and (3) therefore, our feet get cold. His solution is to move the animal heat from our lungs to our feet. Two tubes run from the mouth to the feet. Steiger suggests taking a few quick breaths in the beginning. Then the user should exhale through the mouth. "An easy process," he assures us.

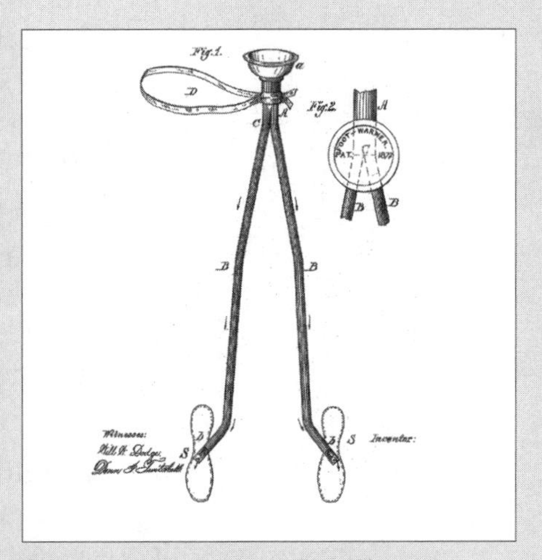

Steiger's Improvement in Foot Warmers

It's a Tough World Out There

You may not know this, but chickens are mean, so mean that they have an irresistible desire to peck the eyes out of their friends' heads. To the rescue is Andrew Jackson, Jr., who in 1902 patented "Certain Useful Improvements in Eye-Protectors for Chickens." The "improved" fowl glasses are made of glass and circle the eyes. They are attached to the chicken's head with an elastic strap. Imagine a pen full of chickens with goggles!

A couple of lessons can be learned from this quick tour through the wonders of human inventions. Be careful about what you invent—you never know when someone will mock you for it. Don't give up on your ideas—they couldn't be more ridiculous than the ones you just read about.

Now look at the PLAN map you made. You can note the important points by writing a summary or by sketching how these inventions could be used. You can also draw another graphic and fill in key words that remind you of main points.

Apply It........... To check your understanding of this article, circle the best answer to each of the following questions.

1. All of the inventions described show that
   - **a.** it is useless to invent new things.
   - **b.** humans can be very clever.
   - **c.** sometimes people don't think about how silly inventions can be.
   - **d.** inventions are not a good way to get rich.

2. The mouse catcher turns into a cheese grater when
   a. mice eat the cheese.
   b. gravity causes the door to drop.
   c. the lids are changed.
   d. two sections become one.

3. In this article, the word *exhale* means
   a. breathe out.
   b. breathe through your nose.
   c. forced breathing.
   d. traveling.

4. You can conclude that the information on egg jerky was included because
   a. the author thought people might like to make it.
   b. it sounded tasty.
   c. it was a good contrast to the other inventions.
   d. it showed that modern inventors invent silly things, too.

Test Tip

Several answers to question 5 might be correct, but only one is the *best* answer. Always read all the answers before choosing one.

5. The writer's tone could *best* be described as
   a. humorous.
   b. angry.
   c. helpful.
   d. serious.

Use the lines below to write your answers for numbers 6 and 7. Your PLAN notes will help you.

6. Which of the inventions you read about might have the best chance of success? Choose one and write a short argument about why it should be produced.

___

___

___

___

7. Does the author think that people should invent new things? Explain your answer.

___

___

___

___

Lesson 4 Biography: Tiny Dynamo Debbie Black

Understand It...... This selection is a biography. Many biographies are written in ways you can predict. Some biographies follow a person's life from birth to death. Others are organized around the events or themes that make the person important. For example, a playwright's biography might focus on her plays. Because you can often predict how a biography will be organized, outlining is a good strategy to use.

Hint

You can review the outlining strategy on page 8.

Try It............... This biography is about Debbie Black. You might not know of her. The title gives you some information though. So does the photograph. Use that information as you preview the biography, looking for major points. As you read, ask yourself questions about how Debbie Black became successful. Read, and then create your outline on a separate piece of paper. Use the outline below as a guide. You may need more Roman numeral lines or more numbered or lettered lines.

Strategy Tip

You might want to set up your outline by writing the subheadings on the Roman numeral lines. Add details about these points on the capital-letter and number lines below each one.

I. ____________
- A. ____________
- B. ____________
  - 1. ____________
  - 2. ____________

II. ____________
- A. ____________
- B. ____________
  - 1. ____________
  - 2. ____________

Tiny Dynamo Debbie Black

"I don't ever let people tell me what I can and cannot do." Debbie Black's words could also be the slogan for her life. At 5 feet 3 inches, Black is the shortest woman in professional basketball. If she had followed other people's advice, she wouldn't be playing today.

Ballet and Basketball

Despite his daughter's pleas, Debbie Black's dad didn't think she belonged on the eighth-grade boys' team he coached. He thought little girls were supposed to take ballet lessons. Black did study ballet, but she wanted to play basketball too. In neighborhood games with the boys on the team, Black played well—very well. "Quite honestly, she would have been the best player," her dad says now.

Growing up with a brother who taught her to be tough helped. "She's definitely not a pretty player," he says today.

"My brothers used to beat me up all the time," Black says. "They never took any mercy on us because we were girls, so we got tough at a very early age." Black's family lives in suburban Philadelphia. Debbie is the youngest child.

Strategy Tip

When you preview, ask yourself some *how* questions. One question might be, "How was Black able to become so successful despite her size?"

When she reached high school, Black joined the basketball team. Once again, the coach tried to talk her out of playing. Once again, she proved she belonged. In 1982, Black led her school to a championship. Regardless of her high school record, college coaches needed some time to believe that this tiny girl could play so well. Finally, though, she won a scholarship.

Black played college ball for St. Joseph's University. She was the talk of Philadelphia—her 12 varsity letters is a school record she holds with her sister Barb. While at St. Joseph's, she led her team to four straight championship seasons. Black had to adjust some parts of her game to become a college star, though. She had been a good scorer in high school, but she wasn't as successful at the college level. Her coach told her: "You do one thing very well. Defense. Get better at it." So she did, becoming a master at stealing the ball.

Black's aggressive, in-your-face style was largely responsible for her success. It was also extremely frustrating to her opponents. Once, she kept stealing the ball from an opposing player. Finally, the player had had enough, Black says. "She just put the ball on her left hip and punched me in the face with her right hand. It knocked me down, but I got right up."

When she was a senior, though, Black couldn't see how she would be able to keep playing basketball after graduation. She was terribly disappointed when she didn't make the 1988 Olympic team. She had never been cut from a team before. "That killed me. It just hurt me," Black says. Then she got a call from a professional women's basketball coach in Australia.

Debbie Black, center

"I Thought You Were Taller!"

The coach had read an article that named Black to a college all-star team—and listed her height as 6 feet 3 inches. The coach, Danny Anderson, coached a team in Tasmania. When he got Black on the phone, she told him her real size. His interest

cooled. Black talked him back into being interested. "Give me a ticket out there," she said to him. "I'll prove myself." He did, and she did.

A year after that, Black's Australian team had gone from being one of the worst teams in the league to being one of the best. Black had worked her magic again. She had also gained a new nickname—the "Tasmanian Devil." Anderson still marvels at his former player's **prowess**. "I've seen her leap over some things Superman couldn't, come out of the stands limping like she needs crutches, tears streaming down her face," he said. "I want to call a sub for her, and she's shaking her head like she's all right."

Vocabulary Tip

You can figure out the meaning of the word *prowess* by looking at how it is used in the sentence. Since Black's coach is marveling at how well she plays, *prowess* probably means "skill."

When the American Basketball League was forming, Black's brother told her about the tryouts. Black had been in Australia eight years and had dual citizenship. She was ready to come home, though. The Colorado Xplosion drafted Black in the sixth round. Her fierce style quickly made her a crowd favorite on her home court. Her employers rewarded her with a five-year, $1.2 million contract.

"Debbie is the most intense player I've ever coached or seen," her current coach says.

"You have to use what you have," Black shrugs. "I'm a pest. That's what's gotten me where I am."

After you finish reading, create your outline. Be sure it shows all of the important points mentioned in the biography. Add details that support each main point. If you need to, revise your outline so it gives you an overview of Debbie Black's life and playing career.

Apply It. . . . . To check your understanding of the biography, circle the best answer to each of the following questions.

1. Debbie Black's father didn't let her play on the boys' basketball team he coached because
   - **a.** he didn't think she was good enough.
   - **b.** girls were not allowed on the team.
   - **c.** the other boys refused to let her play.
   - **d.** he thought she should take ballet lessons instead.
2. When Debbie Black found she couldn't score as well in college as she had in high school, she
   - **a.** practiced shooting until her scoring improved.
   - **b.** decided to become more aggressive.
   - **c.** concentrated on defense instead.
   - **d.** asked her father for advice.

Biography: Tiny Dynamo Debbie Black

3. You can *infer*, or figure out, from this article that Debbie Black's brothers
   a. loved basketball.
   b. helped her grow up to be a competitor.
   c. didn't think she was talented enough to play basketball.
   d. ignored her when she was young.

4. The word that *best* describes Debbie Black is
   a. intense.
   b. sensitive.
   c. smart.
   d. caring.

Test Tip

Question 5 asks what *Debbie Black* believes, not what *you* believe. Think about what she says about her success in the biography.

5. Black believes she's been successful because
   a. she's a strong shooter.
   b. she plays hard.
   c. she refuses to give up.
   d. she practices every day.

Use the lines below to write your answers for numbers 6 and 7. You can use your outline to help you.

6. What events have been most important in Debbie Black's basketball career so far? List them in order. Then write a complete sentence to explain each event.

____

____

____

____

____

7. Write a description of Debbie Black. Include the qualities that have made her such a good player, and explain why they might have helped her.

____

____

____

____

____

Lesson 5 Movie Review: The Vampire Rises—Again and Again

Understand It...... This selection is a movie review. It focuses on movies about vampires. You have probably seen movies about vampires. If not, you might have heard about vampires or read about them. Because you probably know something about vampires, the KWL Plus strategy is a good one to use.

Hint

You can review the KWL Plus strategy on page 4.

Try It............... Use a KWL chart to help you understand the review. Think about what you know about vampires and vampires in the movies before you write in the K column. Write your questions about vampire movies in the W column.

K (What I know)	W (What I want to know)	L (What I've learned)

Max Schreck as Nosferatu

The Vampire Rises—Again and Again

What is it about Dracula? Ever since 1922, when the flickering pictures of *Nosferatu* appeared on silent movie screens across the country, Americans have been thrilled by the bloodsucking vampire. The legend of Dracula still has a strong hold on people. How can you tell? New vampire movies come out all the time.

Since *Nosferatu*, at least 125 movies about vampires have been released. They have come in all varieties. There is *Men of Action Meet Women of Dracula.* You can guess how good that one is. Director Francis Ford Coppola filmed *Bram Stoker's Dracula.* That was a serious look at the story.

Much of the appeal, of course, comes from the character. Like Dracula himself, the Dracula myth just doesn't die. For hundreds of years, people have told tales of vampires. The stories may express the darker part of ourselves. They may also stand for, or *symbolize*, our wish to live forever. Vampires look like us. Often, they act like us. Deep inside, though, vampires are scary and dangerous. Then again, maybe we like vampires for a simpler reason. Maybe we just like to scare ourselves.

Each generation of filmgoers has its own Dracula. The silent movie *Nosferatu*, played by Max Schreck, is scary because the vampire is old and creepy. He has long fingernails and dark eyes. He can communicate only through gestures and captions. *Nosferatu* is an oddly frightening movie, even for today's viewers. The vampire's long fingernails open a locket that has a picture of his victim inside. He smiles—and then his fangs erupt. The caption reads, "My, but she has a lovely neck." When you watch the movie, the line doesn't seem **campy**. It's scary.

Vocabulary Tip

The word *campy* here doesn't mean the kind in the woods. *Campy* is contrasted to *scary.* You can figure out that *campy* probably means something that is the opposite of *scary.*

Movie Review:
The Vampire Rises—Again and Again

Bela Lugosi as Dracula

Vocabulary Tip

The word *anguish* is followed by a phrase that explains the word.

The next major vampire movie appeared in 1931. Bela Lugosi played Dracula. For many, Lugosi still sets the standard for movie vampires. Lugosi's *Dracula* isn't a wonderful movie, but it is important. Lugosi's Hungarian accent launched a million Draculas. Have you ever heard a person trying to sound like a vampire? It's Bela Lugosi the person is imitating. Lugosi's Dracula was different from the pitiful old vampire of *Nosferatu*. Lugosi's Dracula was younger. He looked fine when he dressed up.

Then Dracula fell on hard times. Many films in the next decades were basically awful. Finally, things began to change. In 1979, the silent classic was remade. The new *Nosferatu* was serious in a way that earlier vampire movies had not been. The star, Klaus Kinski, tried to get to the deep soul of Dracula. Kinski wanted to show the character's **anguish**, the vampire's longing for human feelings, for love.

Bram Stoker's Dracula, directed by Francis Ford Coppola in 1992, was a serious movie. Coppola wanted to get to the heart of the novel written by Bram Stoker. That novel was the basis for many vampire movies, including the first *Nosferatu.*

A more modern Dracula is on view in *Interview with the Vampire.* This movie is based on the novel by Anne Rice. When her book by the same name came out, it was a sensation. Suddenly, Dracula was hip again. This Dracula (named Lestat) is young and attractive—no more hairy old men. He's well dressed and could fit into any cool crowd. Crosses don't scare him. Neither does garlic. He does need blood, however. The handsome new vampires look like guys regular women might be thrilled to spend time with. Maybe that's what's so scary about the vampires in this film—they don't stand out in a crowd. They look like us.

Tom Cruise as Lestat

In *Nosferatu,* the viewer sympathizes with the young girls. They were victims. Then Lugosi's Dracula made his appearance. Suddenly, vampires were dangerous, but also a little thrilling. Vampires like Lestat have come a long way from the early days. They look good. You feel they're people, too. These days, vampires are not just among us. They *are* us.

What does all this have to say about our changing society? Nosferatu had fangs and a sneer. Lestat has great clothes and charm. Perhaps we're afraid that evil isn't so clear anymore. Perhaps we're afraid that if Tom Cruise could be a vampire, *anybody* could be a vampire. Maybe we just like to look at young, handsome vampires instead of hairy old men.

When you finish the article, complete the L column of your KWL chart. Then look back at your W questions. See whether they were answered. You may want to reread if you think the answers to your questions might be in the review.

Apply It. . . . . To check your understanding of the review, circle the best answer to each of the following questions.

1. The main point of this article is that
   a. interest in Dracula movies is not very great any more.
   b. the Dracula movies today are much bloodier.
   c. the best vampire movies were made many years ago.
   d. people's interest in vampires remains strong.

Test Tip
Question 2 asks for the difference between the *vampires*, not between the *movies*.

2. The main difference between the vampire in *Nosferatu* and the Bela Lugosi *Dracula* is
   a. one is a silent movie and the other has sound.
   b. the vampire in *Dracula* drinks blood and *Nosferatu* does not.
   c. Dracula is from Europe and Nosferatu is American.
   d. the vampire in *Nosferatu* is an old man and the vampire in *Dracula* is younger and more attractive.

3. When people try to sound like vampires, they are probably imitating
   a. Bela Lugosi.
   b. Bram Stoker.
   c. Nosferatu.
   d. Klaus Kinski.

4. The author considers Lestat to be modern because
   a. he feels nothing for his victims.
   b. he looks like any other attractive young man.
   c. he is a movie star.
   d. he cares about his victims.

Use the lines below to write your answers for numbers 5 and 6. You can use your KWL chart to help you.

Test Tip
To answer question 5, look at all three photographs. How do the vampires look and dress? How scary do they look?

5. Compare and contrast the photographs of vampires in this review.

____

____

____

6. Why do you think people are so interested in vampires? Use information from the article to support your ideas.

____

____

____

Lesson 6 Informational Article: How to Buy a Bike

Understand It......

Hint

You can review the outlining strategy on page 8.

Take a quick look at this article about buying a bike. The subheadings tell you that the article is broken up into several pieces. These pieces are about different things to consider when you shop for a bike. This kind of organization means that outlining could be a good strategy to use to understand the article. The different sections may be the main points in your outline.

Try It..............

The graphic below shows the way an outline is built. First, read the article. Then create your outline. As you work, keep in mind the organization you saw when you previewed the article. Be sure to include not just the main points but also the details that support each point.

I. ____________
  A. ____________
  B. ____________
    1. ____________
    2. ____________
II. ____________
  A. ____________
  B. ____________
    1. ____________
    2. ____________

Strategy Tip

You may find yourself becoming confused about where items belong in your outline. If so, think about the topics of each section in the selection.

How to Buy a Bike

All bikes are not the same. Thinking about the kind of bike you want and doing some research are well worth your time and trouble. If you choose well, you will be satisfied with your purchase for a long time.

When you buy a bike, you need to think about several things. You need to think about your budget. You need to think about where you will ride the bike. That will tell you the kind of bike you need. You also need to think about where to buy it. Finally, you need to know enough about the different parts of the bike to make you an informed buyer.

The Price

Bikes come in all price ranges. People who race their bikes or who ride long distances sometimes pay $200 or more to buy a bike that has all of the extras. People who simply want a bike that they can rely on can pay much less. You might want to look for a used bike in the newspaper or at a used-bike shop.

Where Do You Ride?

The kind of bike you need depends on where and how you ride. The major types of bikes are mountain bikes, road bikes, cruising bikes, and hybrid bikes.

Mountain bikes are increasing in popularity. They are rugged and can take riders just about anywhere. Mountain bikes are the most popular type of bike sold today. They typically have enough gears to allow riders to travel up hills in comfort.

Cruising bikes are best for occasional bike riders. They're most like the bikes of the 1950s. These are the kind of heavy bikes that don't need much care. Choose a cruising bike if you just need a bike once in a while and don't plan to go up many hills. Cruising bikes don't have many gears. These bikes are much cheaper than their fancy cousins.

Road bikes are narrow-wheeled, **lightweight** bikes. You see road bikes in bike races. The seats are high in the air. The ride can be bumpy on any surface that isn't very smooth. Even so, for those who want to ride very fast or very far, a road bike is a good choice.

Vocabulary Tip

The word *lightweight* is made up of two words: *light* and *weight*. Think about what each of these words means. That will tell you what the compound word *lightweight* means.

Hybrid bikes are the bike industry's attempt to join the strength of a mountain bike and the speed of a road bike. The rider can sit more upright, as on a mountain bike. Hybrid bikes are good for people who commute to work. They also work for people who like to ride up hills for fun but don't plan to do it seriously.

Where to Shop

You could buy a bike from a big store that sells many kinds of products, including bikes. You might be sorry, though. Bikes need care. They require tune-ups. Sometimes they need repairs. When your bike needs service, you'll want to take it to someone who knows bikes. That usually means going to a bike store. Buying at a store that will help you take care of your bike makes sense. The people there can also help you choose the right kind of bike for you.

Know Your Bike

You can learn about bikes in many ways. Spend some time in a good bike shop and ask questions. Read books or magazines about bikes. Here are some things you need to keep in mind when you are doing your research.

Find out about brakes. Consider aluminum alloy rim brakes if you ride in areas that are often wet. They will help you stop more quickly in the rain than other types do.

Find out about frames. Bikes with heavy frames can be hard to ride. Lighter bikes have frames made of alloys that are good at absorbing shock.

Find out about gears. Gears matter. The more gears you have, the more easily you can ride up and down hills. Mountain bikes have many gears; road bikes have fewer. If you never ride up hills, however, you won't need to worry much about gears.

If you are a professional rider, you may want the handlebars of a road bike. Most other people prefer to sit upright, which the handlebars on a mountain or hybrid bike let you do.

Don't worry too much about the saddle. That part of the bike isn't too expensive, and a saddle can be changed easily. If the saddle is comfortable, that's all that matters.

Once you know more about the types of bikes available and learn more about their features, you'll be much better able to buy the bike that's right for you!

After you finish your outline, look it over. Make sure it contains the important points and the information that supports each point. Before you answer the questions below, write a summary of what you learned about buying a bike. Use your summary to help you answer the questions.

Apply It........... To check your understanding of the article, circle the best answer to each of the following questions.

1. When you buy a bike, it is important to consider
   a. the size of the wheels.
   b. where and the way you ride.
   c. choosing a bike that you can easily resell.
   d. both a and b.

Test Tip

Underline the most important words in the questions in a test. That will help you pay attention to what the question is asking. In question 2, you might underline *best*.

2. A cruising bike might be best for
   a. someone who is a professional bike rider.
   b. someone who rides occasionally on flat ground.
   c. a child.
   d. someone who plans to ride up hills.

3. In this article, the word *hybrid* means
   a. a combination of two types.
   b. the most expensive.
   c. the easiest to ride.
   d. the best.

4. A good bike shop may
   a. offer better prices and better service.
   b. let you to try out a bike and give you good advice.
   c. offer better salespeople.
   d. offer better service and help you choose the right bike.

5. The author suggests that buyers research bikes by
   a. reading bike magazines.
   b. talking to friends.
   c. consulting professional riders.
   d. getting a money-back guarantee.

Use the lines below to write your answers for numbers 6 and 7. Using your outline can help you.

6. What important factors should you look at when you buy a bike? Include details that support your answer.

____

____

____

____

7. Which type of bike would you most enjoy? Choose one of the four types of bikes and explain why your style matches the bike. Use facts to back up your opinions.

____

____

____

____

Unit 2 Review
Reading in Language Arts

In this unit, you have practiced using the KWL Plus, Outlining, PACA, and PLAN reading strategies. Choose one strategy and use it when you read the selection below. Use a separate sheet of paper to draw charts, take notes, and summarize what you learn.

Hint *Remember that all reading strategies have activities for before, during, and after reading. To review these steps, look back at Unit 1 or at the last page of this book.*

Meet the Beatles

They burst on the scene in 1963 with a song called "I Want to Hold Your Hand." The Beatles not only changed rock and roll. They also set the style for music in the 1960s. Even today, you can hear the Beatles' songs on radio stations across the United States.

From childhood, John Lennon and Paul McCartney both wanted to be musicians. Lennon came from a working-class family in Liverpool, England. McCartney, too, came from a working-class family. McCartney's father was in a jazz band. That influenced McCartney to learn to play the guitar.

Lennon and McCartney met at a church picnic in 1957. Lennon's band, the Quarrymen, was playing at the picnic. First McCartney and then George Harrison joined the group. Drummer Pete Best joined next. In 1960, after several name changes, the band's members decided to name themselves the Beatles.

The Beatles first played in Liverpool, an industrial English city. By May 1962, the group had signed a record contract. Drummer Pete Best had also been replaced by Ringo Starr. The Beatles as we know them were in place.

The British Invasion

When they came to the United States in the early 1960s, the Beatles led what came to be called the "British Invasion." Like other British groups that topped the music charts, the Beatles had been influenced by U.S. musicians, such as Chuck Berry.

The Beatles' first hits, such as "I Want to Hold Your Hand," were simple, fresh, and catchy. The Beatles became a national craze. Girls fainted at the sight of the group.

The Beatles then led the way to a more experimental era in music. The late 1960s was not a time for cute, catchy tunes. There was a growing feeling of rebellion among young people.

In 1967, the Beatles' album *Sergeant Pepper's Lonely Hearts Club Band* set new standards for albums.

It was the first of what are now called "concept" albums. On a concept album, all of the songs are based on one theme. The songs on *Sergeant Pepper's* were unusual and haunting. In addition, the Beatles added electronic music and the Indian sitar.

The Team of Lennon and McCartney

Much of the group's success is due to the team of Lennon and McCartney. Lennon was known as the thinker of the group. He was the one who pushed the others to new ground. His songs were more experimental. McCartney was the master of melodies and words that touched the heart. Together, they were one of the most important songwriting teams in history. Their songs have been sung around the world.

Use your notes and charts to help you answer the questions below.

1. What was the name of the Beatles' first hit song?

a. "Sergeant Pepper's"
b. "Meet the Beatles"
c. "I Want to Hold Your Hand"
d. "British Invasion"

2. Which is the best description of the team of Lennon and McCartney?

a. Lennon wrote the words; McCartney was the thinker.
b. Both Lennon and McCartney took risks with their songwriting.
c. Lennon's songs were experimental; McCartney's songs touched the heart.
d. Lennon kept McCartney from writing songs that were too unusual.

3. Which of the following did *not* lead to the Beatles' success?

a. They became the favorites of teenage girls.
b. Lennon and McCartney were a brilliant songwriting team.
c. The Beatles' music became more experimental in the late 1960s.
d. Their record company helped them perform on television.

4. How was *Sergeant Pepper's* different from other albums at the time?

____

____

5. Name another music group that you think has changed the style for music. Explain your choice.

____

____

Unit 3
Reading in Social Studies

You already read many kinds of social studies texts, both in school and out of school. In school, you read social studies textbooks. Outside school, you might read newspapers and magazine articles about news events. When you plan a trip, you might read about the weather and about the people who live at your destination. Reading in social studies is a skill you will use often.

How Social Studies Reading Is Organized

Within social studies, there are several subjects. You are likely to read about history, geography, economics, citizenship, and culture. Although these subjects focus on different topics, you will see some patterns in the ways that social studies readings are organized. You may see all these patterns in one selection. Seeing patterns in the ways readings are organized can help you know what to expect. Here are some common patterns that writers of social studies use.

Sequence of Events. Some social studies texts are written in chronological, or time, order. When you see this pattern, you will notice that the events are presented in the order in which they occurred. Timelines like the one below can help you understand this pattern.

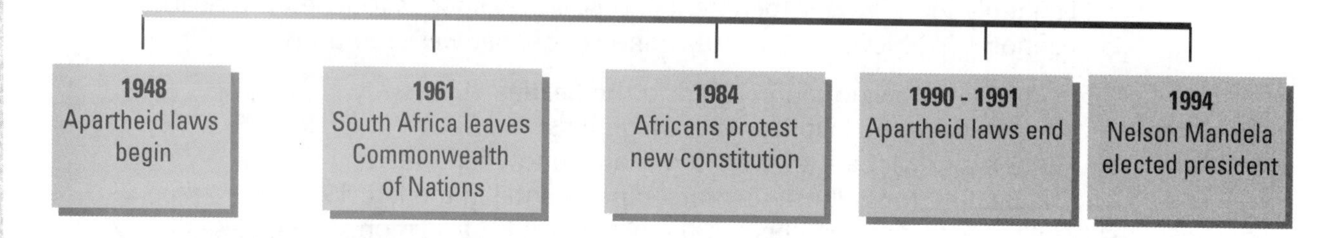

Cause and Effect. Major events in history may cause many later events. Sometimes social studies texts present history as a series of causes and effects. Understanding these links can help you understand why events occurred. The drawing on page 47 shows you how a series of causes and effects can work together to make a chain.

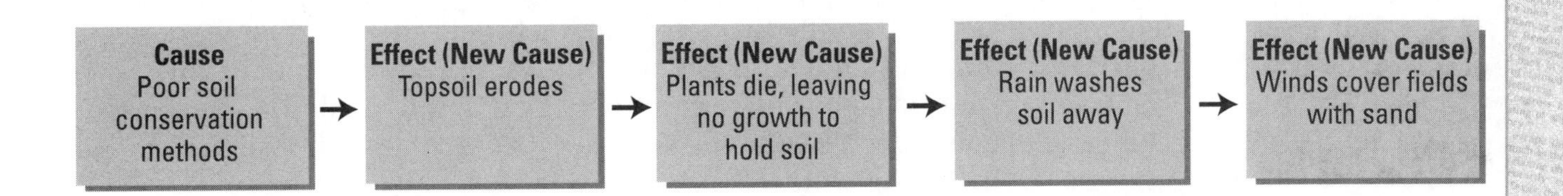

Compare and Contrast. This pattern is common in citizenship and geography books. You may read about the similarities and differences between two forms of government or two cultures. Recognizing this pattern can help you understand the similarities and differences that the text is pointing out. Below is a drawing of how an article might be organized that compares and contrasts two time periods.

1950s
two-parent families,
mother usually worked at home,
parents knew all answers

same
most scenes in living room or kitchen,
kids respect parents' advice,
families get along most of the time

1990s
single-parent families,
mother works outside the home,
kids often correct parents

Getting the Most from Your Reading

If you can recognize the way a reading is organized, you will be better able to understand it. You will be able to think about what kind of information might be next and how all the points in the reading fit together. Making drawings like the ones on these two pages can show you these patterns. Thinking about how a reading is organized can help you understand—and remember—what you read.

Lesson 7 History: The Underground Railroad

Understand It...... The PLAN strategy should help you understand this selection because you can choose the graphic that makes sense to you. First, preview this selection. If it's written in chronological, or time, order, use the sequence chart. If it compares and contrasts two things, use the Venn diagram. If it focuses on one topic, a wheel-and-spoke diagram could be your best choice. Once you decide how the selection is organized, choose the graphic you think best fits it.

Hint
You can review the PLAN strategy on page 16.

Try It.............. Remember that when you use the PLAN strategy, you preview to find out more about what you'll be reading. You use that information to predict what the main points may be. You use the information about the main points to sketch your graphic. Then you read again, locating important information. You put check marks next to information you know something about and question marks next to information you know little about. Finally, you add information that supports the main points. If you missed main points, add them, too.

Below you'll find three possible PLAN graphics. You can use one of them or create a graphic of your own.

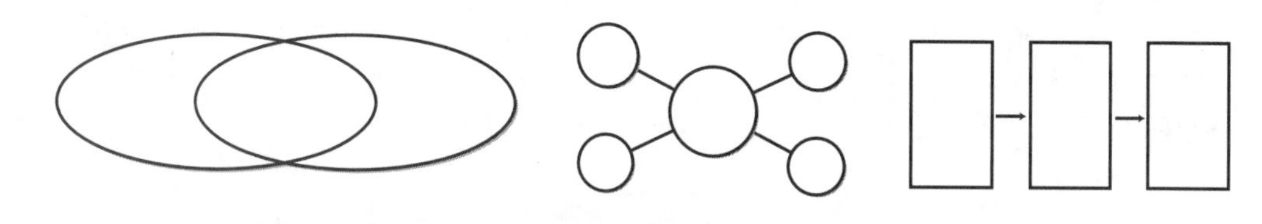

Strategy Tip
If you put a question mark in front of a point, make sure you understand it by the time you finish reading.

Vocabulary Tip
You might not know what *bounty hunters* are. However, you know what *hunters* are. Who might chase enslaved people? Those who returned enslaved people could claim a *bounty*, or reward.

The Underground Railroad

They traveled by night. They had only the North Star to guide them. For the people who escaped slavery on the Underground Railroad, darkness kept danger at bay. The dark was a friend. It kept the **bounty hunters** away. It kept the dogs and the guns away.

The Best Path to Freedom

Enslaved people desperate for freedom had two choices. They could try to escape on their own. They could also use the Underground Railroad. The Underground Railroad was the best-known path to freedom. It was set up in the 1780s by Quakers, and it helped tens of thousands of enslaved people to escape to freedom.

The escapees planned their path by thinking of people who could help them. They traveled between farms, called "stations." Those traveling on the railroad also stopped in towns where networks of people had been set up. The people who helped were called "conductors." Sometimes they were whites who held a deep belief that slavery was wrong. At other times, free African Americans aided the travelers.

Once escapees arrived at a safe place, they were given food and a bed. Then they were hidden. The next night they continued their journey. At each spot, they were directed to the next haven.

Some enslaved people traveled to free Northern states. The Underground Railroad might take an escapee to a border town such as Wilmington, Delaware. Delaware was a slave state. Beyond it was New Jersey. That state was free. Another popular destination was Canada. No slavery was allowed there. At places such as Buffalo, New York, escapees were able to travel across water to Canada. Once there, they were free.

Freedom for All

Some conductors on the Underground Railroad became famous for their courage and determination. Harriet Tubman is one example. When she was young, Tubman was enslaved. She escaped to the North. Then she began leading others to freedom. She made 19 journeys, leading 300 escapees to Canada and to freedom.

Strategy Tip

Because there is a photo of Harriet Tubman, you can assume she's an important figure in the selection. What information about Tubman can you add to your PLAN graphic?

Harriet Tubman

The Underground Railroad helped many people escape slavery. In addition, it aided the cause of freedom for all enslaved people. People working for the Underground Railroad helped whites in the North understand the agony of slavery. Whites increasingly refused to obey such laws as the Fugitive Slave Act. This act forced escapees to return to slavery. Stories of the terrible lives of enslaved people made some whites in the North turn their backs on people who supported slavery.

The success of the Underground Railroad helped lead to the Civil War. More and more people in the North refused to return enslaved people to slavery. Southerners, in turn, passed more laws to force people to capture and return escapees. Most people in the South were furious about being told that their way of life was wrong. The rage and fury people felt about slavery in both the North and the South helped fuel the Civil War.

When you finish the selection, look back at your graphic. Add the main points and the supporting information you need to understand the selection. Once you are satisfied you understand what you read, use a review technique such as writing a summary or making a list to review what you've learned about the Underground Railroad.

Apply It........... To check your understanding of the selection, circle the best answer to each of the following questions.

1. The main idea of this selection is that
   - **a.** Harriet Tubman was a famous conductor on the Underground Railroad.
   - **b.** the Underground Railroad was the main cause of the Civil War.
   - **c.** the Underground Railroad was an important way for people to escape slavery.
   - **d.** both b and c
2. A *station* on the Underground Railroad was
   - **a.** a place where escapees could safely rest.
   - **b.** Canada, where slavery was illegal.
   - **c.** an actual railroad station where escapees could catch a train to Canada or a free state.
   - **d.** a new home for escapees.

Test Tip

Question 3 asks what the word *haven* means. Read the sentence and substitute each possible definition for the word *haven*. See which choice makes sense in the sentence.

3. The word *haven* in the section "The Best Path to Freedom" means
   - **a.** a farm.
   - **b.** a safe place.
   - **c.** a plantation.
   - **d.** a border state.
4. The Underground Railroad helped
   - **a.** enslaved people earn their rights.
   - **b.** enslaved people gain their freedom.
   - **c.** people in the North understand the agony of slavery.
   - **d.** both b and c
5. You can infer that the Fugitive Slave Act
   - **a.** allowed enslaved people to go to free states.
   - **b.** helped Southerners return escapees to slavery.
   - **c.** was supported by the North.
   - **d.** was never enforced.

Use the lines below to write your answers for numbers 6 and 7. Use your PLAN graphic to help you.

6. Describe a danger that slaves who escaped faced on their journey to freedom.

   ____

   ____

7. What can you infer about Harriet Tubman from reading this selection?

   ____

   ____

Lesson 8 Sociology: What Do You Mean?

Understand It...... What does the title of this article tell you about its topic? You might guess that the article has something to do with communication. To check your guess, look at the subheadings. What do they tell you?

Hint
You can review the outlining strategy on page 8.

Try It.............. Now preview the article to get a clearer idea of what you will be reading about. By looking at the subheadings and terms in bold type, you can see that the article is about how body language differs among cultures. You can also see that it is organized by regions of the world. Because the order is easy to understand, this article would be a good one to outline. You might write each subheading on a separate capital-letter line of your outline. List supporting details on the number and small-letter lines underneath.

Strategy Tip
Remember that when you preview an article, you simply look at headings, subheadings, topic sentences, and any words that catch your eye. These things can offer you clues to the article's topic and organization.

I. ____________________
  A. ____________________
  B. ____________________
    1. ____________________
    2. ____________________
II. ____________________
  A. ____________________
  B. ____________________
    1. ____________________
    2. ____________________

What Do You Mean?

The two businessmen are talking. The man from Saudi Arabia moves closer. The American backs up. The Saudi Arabian moves in. Frowning, the American moves back. Looking annoyed, the Saudi Arabian moves still closer. The deal they are discussing is in trouble, and neither one knows why.

The problem is space—personal space. Americans stand a few feet away from each other when they talk. They're more at ease when they keep a little space between them. People in the Middle East stand much closer when they talk. The American felt cornered. The Saudi Arabian felt insulted. He thought the American was being distant. Neither one understood what was going on.

Vocabulary Tip
In this paragraph, definitions appear in two different ways. The definition for the phrase *body language* is inside of the dashes that follow it. The definition for the word *gestures* is between the pair of commas that follow it.

Today, people from different cultures often work together. Knowing **body language**—or unspoken signals—from different parts of the world can be important. It can also be important to know what **gestures**, or hand signals, mean in different places. You may think you are saying hello. The other person may see a deep insult. Here is a quick look at some of the signs and signals you should know if you travel. You could save a friendship—or a business deal.

Sociology: What Do You Mean?

Middle East

People in the Middle East not only like to stand close to one another, they also like to touch. Men may touch arms. They may even hold hands, which means only that they are friends.

Many people in the Middle East also think that the left hand is unclean. Use the right hand when you eat. When you hand something to someone, use your right hand.

Be careful about saying nice things about objects. You may tell someone you like his briefcase. He will probably give it to you.

Watch how you sit. Do not show the sole of your shoe to the person you are with. That is considered to be impolite.

Asia

This part of the world is very large. People from many different cultures live in Asia. Do not make the mistake of thinking all Asians have the same ideas about good behavior. They don't.

However, some things are generally true. In Asia, being polite, or "**saving face,**" is very important. Never make another person look foolish or "lose face." The Asian sense of politeness comes out in other ways. People often tell you what they think you want to hear.

Vocabulary Tip

You might not know the phrase *saving face*, but it is explained in this paragraph in several ways. If you don't understand a word or phrase, look to see whether it is explained in the sentences near it.

Central America and South America

As in Asia, there are great variations among the peoples of this region. Central America and South America have more than 40 countries. However, people in this region still have some customs in common.

Being on time is usually not thought to be important. Often, meetings start at least a half hour after they were set to begin. Just remember that people are not being rude.

As in the Middle East, people here stand close to one another. Try not to seem uncomfortable. If you move back, you may be seen as being rude. Hugging is common. So is the sight of businessmen walking arm-in-arm.

Making Body Language Work for You

No matter where in the world travelers go, they should watch and learn the local customs. For instance, they should find out how far apart people usually stand when they talk. They should avoid hand gestures until they understand their meaning in that country. A friendly wave in the United States may be cause for a fight somewhere else.

Travelers could also quietly watch people in the country they're visiting. Observing how people talk to one another can help you make friends, or business deals, in a foreign country.

Look over your outline to make sure it shows all the major points mentioned in the article. Then use your outline to write a summary of what you've read. Your summary will help you review the article.

Apply It

To check your understanding of this article, circle the best answer to each of the following questions.

1. People in the Middle East and Central America are similar because both believe
   a. that politeness is the most important trait.
   b. that people should stand close when they talk.
   c. that being on time is not that important.
   d. both a and c.

Test Tip

The word *space* in question 2 has more than one meaning. When you are asked to define a word with more than one meaning, review all the meanings you know. Decide which one makes sense in the sentence.

2. The word *space* in the second paragraph refers to
   a. outer space.
   b. space between people.
   c. a barrier.
   d. to be unaware.

3. The main point of this article is that
   a. when you are in another country, you shouldn't be alarmed if someone moves close to you in conversation.
   b. customs and body language vary greatly from one country to another.
   c. "saving face" is important throughout the world.
   d. businesspeople must never show that they are alarmed by the behavior of people from other countries.

4. People in the Middle East do not use the left hand to give things to people because
   a. the left hand is sacred.
   b. the left hand is awkward.
   c. it is an ancient tradition.
   d. the left hand is considered to be unclean.

Use the lines below to write your answers for numbers 5 and 6. Your outline and your summary will help you.

5. Describe how body language can lead people from different countries to misunderstand one another.

____

____

6. Write a list of instructions to someone who will visit one area discussed in this article. Be sure to discuss polite and impolite behavior.

____

____

Lesson 9 Geography: The Chocolate Journey

Understand It...... This geography selection tells how chocolate was brought from South America to Europe. The word *journey* in the title tells you that you might learn about a series of events. Outlining is a good strategy to use for selections that are organized in chronological, or time, order.

Hint

You can review the outlining strategy on page 8.

Try It.............. Preview the selection, looking at the subheadings and the map. What do you notice about the way the selection is organized? On a separate piece of paper, create an outline after you read. Use the graphic below to remind you of the way an outline is set up.

I. ____________
  A. ____________
  B. ____________
    1. ____________
    2. ____________
II. ____________
  A. ____________
  B. ____________
    1. ____________
    2. ____________

The Chocolate Journey

Vocabulary Tip

What does *nobles* mean? You may be able to figure out the meaning from nearby words. Also think about the meaning of *noble* you already know.

Imagine this scene. A servant brings a cup of a new precious liquid into the room where the Spanish **nobles** are sitting. One noble lifts the cup to his lips. So began the passion for chocolate that gripped Spain in the 1500s and later spread throughout Europe.

An Early American Favorite

Chocolate had long been a favorite drink in the Americas. Cacao trees originally grew in the river valleys of South America. In the seventh century, the Maya carried the trees and their seeds, cocoa beans, north into Mexico. The beans became so popular, they were used as money.

In 1502, Columbus made his fourth voyage to the Americas. He was the first explorer to take cocoa back to Spain. In 1519, a man who had sailed with the explorer and conqueror of Mexico, Hernán Cortés, tasted chocolate. Cortés's man saw Montezuma drink chocolate. The drink was served in golden cups, the explorer wrote. When he returned to Europe, Cortés's man told many people about this wonderful new drink.

The Columbian Exchange

The drink Cortés's man tried was not the cocoa we know. It had no sugar or milk. Instead, it was made with cocoa, red pepper, vanilla, and water. Even so, cocoa made its way back to Europe. The movement of

Strategy Tip

What does the map tell you about the Columbian Exchange? Add this information to your outline.

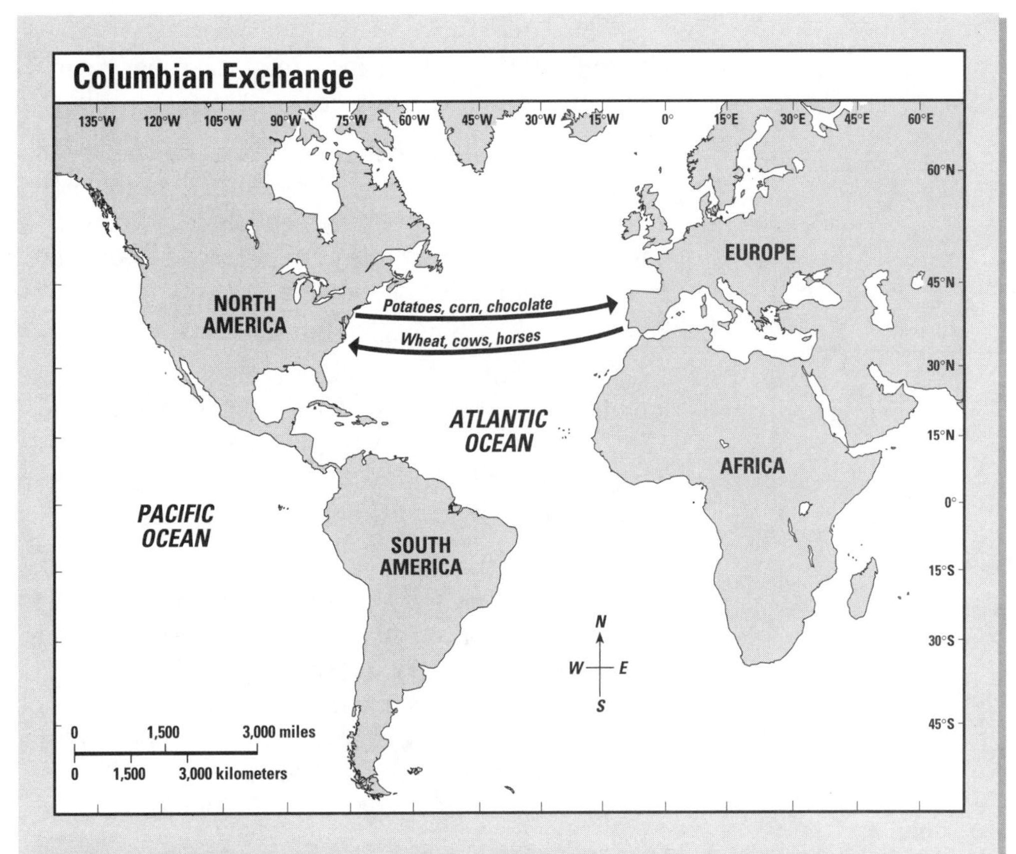

chocolate is part of the Columbian Exchange, which was named after Columbus. The Columbian Exchange was a network of trade Columbus began that linked the Americas and Europe. It developed as a result of the explorations of Columbus and many other explorers.

From the beginning of his journeys, Columbus took items he found in the Americas back to Europe. He loaded tomatoes, sweet potatoes, and pumpkins onto his ships. He carried squash and beans and tobacco and chocolate. When he returned to the Americas, Columbus brought horses, cows, and pigs from Europe. He also brought wheat and barley and sugar cane to the Americas.

The Columbian Exchange changed the world. The foods travelers found on their explorations began to be grown in Europe. The "new" foods spread to West Africa and China. Corn, potatoes, and beans became important foods for people all over the world. The discoveries of new food sources probably contributed to the global rise in population that began about then.

Chocolate's Popularity Grows

Once chocolate arrived in Europe, the people there began trying new things. They added sugar, cinnamon, cloves, and vanilla to the cocoa. The first factories to turn the beans into paste opened in Spain about 1580. Spain kept the secret for a few years. The drink had a great following among the nobility.

The secret of hot chocolate could not be kept for long. Outside Spain, people added only water, sugar, and vanilla to their cocoa. At first, the drink was sold in coffee houses in London. Then fancy chocolate houses began to open. By the 1600s, the drink was a favorite of the upper classes in France and England. Within a few decades, hot chocolate was the rage of Europe.

The idea of adding milk to chocolate might have come from Jamaica. A doctor named Sir Hans Sloane lived there from 1687 to 1689. He saw young children being given a chocolate drink with milk in it. When Sloane returned to England, he told everyone about the drink. He became a big booster of hot chocolate with milk.

Chocolate Today

Europe became a world leader in the production of chocolate. A Dutch man invented a way to make cocoa powder. The first chocolate bar was made in 1819 in Switzerland. The manufacturer was Francois-Louis Cailler. In 1878, a writer remarked that chocolate candy was very popular. Today, chocolate remains many people's favorite. The many foods made from the bitter beans carried to Europe by Columbus still give pleasure to people all over the world.

Look over your outline. Does it include all the important information you learned while reading? If you need to, read again and revise your outline so that it gives a quick overview of the selection. When you finish your outline, you should have a good idea of how chocolate journeyed from the Old World to the New World.

Apply It............ To check your understanding of the selection, circle the best answer to each of the following questions.

1. Which of these statements is true?
   - **a.** The cacao tree came originally from Mexico.
   - **b.** Corn came from Europe.
   - **c.** Wheat came from Europe.
   - **d.** Cortés was the first explorer to take chocolate to Europe.
2. From his description of the way the cocoa was served, you can conclude that Cortés's man
   - **a.** was eager to bring the beverage to Europe.
   - **b.** thought Montezuma's court was wasteful.
   - **c.** was impressed with the way it was served.
   - **d.** wasn't interested in anything he saw.

3. The Columbian Exchange is named
   a. for the Columbians, who introduced chocolate to Europe.
   b. for Columbus, who began it.
   c. for Cortés, who began it.
   d. for Columbia, which was the first land Columbus visited.
4. You might conclude that chocolate was a favorite of the nobility in the 1500s because
   a. it was expensive, and only the rich could afford it.
   b. Columbus was a member of the nobility and introduced it to his friends.
   c. others were afraid to drink something from another country.
   d. poor people were not allowed to drink it.
5. The word *rage* in the second paragraph of the section "Chocolate's Popularity Grows" means
   a. anger.
   b. happiness.
   c. an unpopular thing.
   d. a very popular thing.

Test Tip

Unless the instructions tell you otherwise, always use complete sentences when you answer a short-answer question.

Use the lines below to write your answers for numbers 6 and 7. You can use the map in this lesson and your outline to help you.

6. Summarize chocolate's journey from the Americas to Europe. How did it reach Europe, and how did it become popular there?

____

____

____

____

____

7. Write a definition of the Columbian Exchange. Explain how people in Europe and the Americas might have benefited from it.

____

____

____

____

____

Lesson 10 Civics: The Celebration Experiment

Understand It...... Almost everyone has had some contact with the Walt Disney Company. Many people have seen Disney movies. Others have been to a Disney theme park. Disney is part of America. That is one reason the KWL Plus strategy works for this article about Disney's planned city of Celebration in Florida.

Hint

You can review the KWL Plus strategy on page 4.

Try It............... Draw a KWL chart like the one below on a separate sheet of paper. Write some key words in the K column about things you already know about the Walt Disney Company or about Celebration, the town that Disney built. Now, preview the article. Write what you want to know about this topic in the W column. Then read the article. After you do, fill in the L column with what you learned. When you have completed your chart, remember to write a summary of the article to help you remember what you've learned.

Strategy Tip

When you use the KWL Plus strategy, you combine what you know with what you would like to know. In this lesson, think about what you already know about The Walt Disney Company. How do you think Disney would design a city?

K (What I know)	W (What I want to know)	L (What I've learned)

The Celebration Experiment

What happens when Mickey Mouse meets politics? The answer is Celebration, Florida. This new city was built by Disney. Every detail has been planned, even the color of the curtains people may hang in their windows. Everything is perfect. Or is it? Can a company run a town? That is the question Celebration hopes to answer.

Part of the answer, of course, has to do with the company. Almost everyone in the United States probably has an opinion about Disney. To some, *Disney* means clean, wholesome entertainment. It means warm feelings. It means organization. It means that every detail is in place. To others, *Disney* means too much organization. It means forced happiness. It means nothing above average. It means boring.

You can probably guess how the two groups feel about Celebration. The pro-Disney group is lining up to get in. The anti-Disney group is warning of grim results. The interesting question, though, is whether a company used to managing theme parks will be able to manage a town. In Celebration, Disney can't fire anyone. The company can't force people to do what they don't want to do.

The Disney Dream

Celebration is not a new idea. The form it took is new. For years, Walt Disney dreamed of building a city of the future. In Disney's mind,

that city would be built under a dome. It would have skyscrapers. Residents would travel by monorail. No retirees would be allowed. Nobody would own property. Instead, the city would be home to young renters. Before that town was built, however, Walt Disney died.

The city that has risen from the ground in Florida is very different from Walt Disney's dream city. Celebration is intended to remind people of a simpler time. Disney is trying to sell the city as a return to a simpler time. The dream is that this would be a place where neighbors sit on their front porches and talk to one another. In this new community, crime would be low and neighbors would be friendly.

Vocabulary Tip

Notice that the definition for *utopia*, "a place where life is perfect," appears between commas right after the word.

To create that **utopia**, a place where life is perfect, Disney put some very good minds to work. The company hired some of the best designers in the business. It hired nationally known architects. What some of those people are doing in Celebration is a dream for them, too. Many architects have long argued that suburbs are not the best places to live. They say that suburbs isolate people. People drive into their garages, go into their houses, and never come out.

Vocabulary Tip

The word *principle* has a homophone, *principal*. These words are spelled differently and have different meanings, but they sound the same. You can tell which one is correct by reading the sentence and deciding which meaning makes more sense.

Celebration was designed with older **principles** in mind. Houses have front porches. Streets are designed so neighbors can meet. That is what people like, the planners say. Their aim is to keep the best of the old ways of designing cities. There is a name for this design theory: New Urbanism.

The New Reality

Disney's town attracted attention from the moment it was announced. For some people, just knowing Disney was involved made the project look great. Others liked the idea of creating an old-time town. Still others looked at the state-of-the-art school and decided to buy in Celebration.

Disney's town, Celebration

Many people joined a lottery to buy housing there. That there was a lottery at all is noteworthy. People wanted to live in this town. There will be 8,000 homes there finally. The population will be 15,000 to 20,000. Housing isn't cheap, either. A house here costs more than in the areas around Celebration.

Most of the people who first came out to see the new town were upper- or middle-class whites. Although Disney plans to provide places for people who have less money, there is no housing for poor people.

One of the unusual aspects of the town is that there will be no city government. The county will take care of water and sewers. Disney will take care of everything else. The company promises to listen to the homeowners' group. That group will pass judgment on people who break rules. Those rules include what color homes can be painted. One woman decided not to fight, and she took her red curtains down. Another couple fought for their right to have a front door that is different from the plans—and won.

Some of the residents think the idea of Disney control is great. They think Disney will make the right decisions. They trust Disney more than any politicians, they say. On the other hand, real life is messy. Things happen in a real town that don't happen in a theme park.

People who follow local politics are watching the growth of Celebration with great interest. Can Disney make it work? Can it really replace government? Can Disney govern better than politicians? The future of this Florida town has a lot to teach anyone who is interested in democracy in America.

Now review your KWL chart. Did you find answers to all your questions? If you didn't, you may want to look back at the article. You can also find articles about Disney and Celebration in magazines and on the Internet. Then use your KWL chart to write a summary of the article. Use the summary and your KWL chart to help you answer the following questions.

Apply It. . . . . To check your understanding of the article, circle the best answer to each of the following questions.

1. Walt Disney's ideas for a town included
   a. front porches on every house.
   b. skyscrapers and a monorail.
   c. a population with many different ages of people.
   d. home ownership for everyone.

Test Tip

Question 2 asks for the main idea of the article. When a question asks for the main idea, more than one answer may have correct information, but only one answer is the *main idea* of the article.

2. The main idea of this article is that
   a. Celebration has attracted attention from around the country.
   b. the Disney company has created another brilliant idea.
   c. Celebration is an experiment to see if a company can run a town.
   d. Celebration will make huge profits for Disney.

3. The phrase *New Urbanism* in the section "The Disney Dream" means
   a. keeping the best of the old ways of designing cities.
   b. mixing old and new design ideas.
   c. finding new ways of designing cities.
   d. making sure that everyone in a city can get onto the highway.

4. People who said they were interested in living in Celebration
   a. were often interested because of the Disney name.
   b. wanted to buy in an affordable area.
   c. usually didn't know Disney had created the town.
   d. wanted to move there because the town would be modern.

5. The author believes that the most interesting question about Celebration is whether
   a. Disney can make a profit.
   b. a big corporation can successfully replace government.
   c. people will be happy living in a town run by a company.
   d. the New Urbanism will work.

Use the lines below to write your answers for numbers 6 and 7. You can use your KWL chart to help you.

6. What are the major arguments for and against Celebration? Summarize them here.

____

____

____

____

____

7. Why do you think the idea of Celebration changed so much from Walt Disney's original dream? Support your ideas.

____

____

____

____

____

Lesson 11 History: America's Secret Weapon in World War II

Understand It...... This history article tells a story about a group of heroes of World War II. The PLAN strategy should help you understand the article because you can choose the graphic that works best for you. First, preview this article to find out how it is organized. If you think it's written in chronological, or time, order, use a sequence chart. If you think it compares and contrasts two things, use a Venn diagram. If it focuses on one topic, a wheel-and-spoke diagram could be your best choice. Once you decide how the article is organized, you can choose the graphic you think best fits it.

Hint
You can review the PLAN strategy on page 16.

Try It.............. Remember that when you use the PLAN strategy, you predict what the main points of the article might be. Below you'll find three possible PLAN graphics. You can use one of them or create a graphic of your own. Remember to make your graphic large enough so you can add notes. Do the first three steps of the PLAN method: predict, locate information, and add key words. If you find the graphic you've chosen doesn't work, try another graphic.

Strategy Tip
When you create a graphic, you may get halfway into it and realize it doesn't work. Don't keep going. Try another type of graphic.

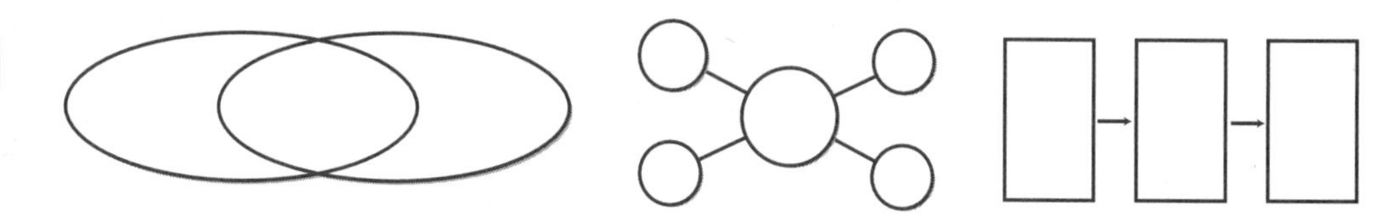

America's Secret Weapon in World War II

The time was World War II. The United States was fighting Japan, and the U.S. Marines had a difficult problem. They had to find a way to keep their communications secret. Japan kept breaking the U.S. codes. An order would go out: Attack there. The Japanese would pick up the message on their radios and decipher the code. They knew their enemy's plan, so they had time to prepare.

The Americans became desperate as the Japanese broke code after code. Then Philip Johnson went to the Marines. He had an idea. Johnson had grown up on a Navajo reservation. He knew the language, and he knew it was very hard to learn. Fewer than 30 non-Navajos knew it. None of them were Japanese.

A New Idea

Johnson thought Navajo could work well as a code for several reasons. Navajo is unwritten. It has no alphabet. It is very complex. A word spoken in four different ways can have four different meanings. The Marine officer was not sure about Johnson's idea. Even so, he agreed to give it a try. The Marines had to try *something*.

Vocabulary Tip
Code Talkers is a made-up compound word. You know what the parts of the word mean, though, so you can figure out the meaning.

Johnson set up a test. He showed what could be done in 20 seconds. The Navajos could encode, transmit, and decode a three-line message. The officer was impressed. The machines that did the job took a half hour. The Marines brought in two of their code breakers. The code breakers didn't even know how to write down what they were hearing. Trying to translate it was impossible. The Navajo **Code Talkers** had a job. The officer ordered 200 Navajos to be trained for code-talking duty.

In May 1942, the first 29 recruits created the Navajo code. It was based on the Navajo language. The code could not be understood by a native speaker who was not trained, though. The code included words created to represent military terms. For example, *submarine* became "iron fish." The Navajos memorized the code. Then 27 Code Talkers were sent to the Pacific. Two stayed behind to teach new recruits. Before the war was over, 400 Navajos had served as Code Talkers.

Vocabulary Tip
What does the word *frustrated* mean in this sentence? Think about the sentences around it. How might the Japanese have felt if they were unable to break this one code?

Their success has become legendary. The system was simple. Two Code Talkers talked to each other. They passed on information about where troops were going. They explained what was happening. And they **frustrated** the Japanese. The Japanese broke the Army and Navy codes. The Marine code remained unbroken.

Making a Name

The Code Talkers made their name at Iwo Jima, where one of the most important battles of the war was fought. In that battle, 4,189 Americans were killed and 15,308 were injured. On the Japanese side, 22,000 were killed.

During the first two days of the battle, six Code Talkers worked around the clock. They coded 800 messages. Not one was wrong. Major Howard Connor was the signal officer for that battle. "Were it not for the Navajos," he said, "the Marines would never have taken Iwo Jima."

In 1968, the Marines finally told the Code Talkers' story. It had been a classified secret until then. When a high-ranking Japanese official found out about the Code Talkers, he said, "Thank you. That is a puzzle I thought would never be solved."

In 1983, President Ronald Reagan honored the Code Talkers. In 1992, the Pentagon set up an exhibit that shows the history of the code. The Code Talkers have gradually gained the respect they deserve.

After you read, note what you learned. Revise your graphic if you need to. Then review your work to make sure you understand what you have read.

History: America's Secret Weapon in World War II

Apply It............ To check your understanding of this article, circle the best answer to each of the following questions.

1. Philip Johnson thought the Navajo language would work as a code because
   a. Navajo words can have several different meanings.
   b. Navajo is a very complex language with no alphabet.
   c. the Navajo language was known by the Japanese.
   d. both a and b
2. Military officials were not sure about using the Navajo code because
   a. they thought there were not enough native Navajo speakers.
   b. they had never heard of a code like that before.
   c. they didn't know how to write it down.
   d. they thought the Japanese could easily break it.
3. The phrase *decipher the code* in the first paragraph means
   a. figure out the code.
   b. change the code.
   c. adjust the code.
   d. replace the code.
4. The main point of this article is that
   a. the Navajo Code Talkers fought bravely in World War II.
   b. the Navajo Code Talkers created an unbreakable code in World War II.
   c. the Code Talkers did not get the recognition they deserved.
   d. the Japanese admitted they lost the war because of the Code Talkers.
5. The code the Navajo Code Talkers used
   a. translated Navajo into English.
   b. could be understood by any Navajo.
   c. was based on the Navajo language.
   d. is still used in military communications.

Test Tip

Turn back to the first paragraph of the article. Reread the sentence about deciphering the code. Now substitute each choice in question 3 in that sentence. Which choice makes sense?

Use the lines below to write your answers for numbers 6 and 7. You can use your PLAN notes to help you.

6. How did the Navajo Code Talkers frustrate the Japanese?

____

____

____

7. Summarize the story of how the Navajo Code Talkers came to exist.

____

____

____

Lesson 12 Economics: The Cola Wars

Understand It...... Even if you've never tasted a Coke or Pepsi, you've probably heard about the huge companies that make and sell the drinks. Their ads are everywhere. So are their products. Because you already are at least somewhat familiar with the products, the PACA strategy is a good one to use to understand this selection.

Hint
You can review the PACA strategy on page 12.

Try It.............. Preview the selection. Pay close attention to the heads and the graph. Then create a PACA chart like the one below. Write in your predictions in the Predictions column. After you read, find the predictions you made that were correct. Add checks next to your correct predictions. Add to or revise your predictions. Put stars next to these items. Then add support for your predictions in the Support column.

Predictions	Support

The Cola Wars

The opponents battle, commercial to commercial, around the world. They take no prisoners. At stake is one of the richest markets in the world. This is the cola war.

The cola war isn't just between Coke and Pepsi. It is also between soft drinks and every other beverage in the world. That includes water. How serious is this battle? Douglas Ivester is the head of Coca-Cola. He recently told an industry gathering that, on average, people drink 64 ounces of liquid a day. Only four ounces of this amount is soft drinks. Ivester sees an opportunity. "That still leaves our industry with 60 ounces to go after," he said. "Put another way—we're only tapping four 64ths of that opportunity."

Coke wants to make sure that people choose Coke, not Pepsi. Over the years, the two companies have tried a variety of ways to make people believe that their product is the best. For most people, though, choosing a soft drink is not a big deal—so Coke and Pepsi have to make it a big deal. In recent years, the two giants have used two very different battle plans.

Economics: The Cola Wars

Vocabulary Tip

Sometimes words are followed by a definition. Notice the definition of *diversification* in this paragraph. The word *core* in the next paragraph is also followed by a definition.

Strategy Tip

In economics, graphs often provide information that leads you to the point of the selection.

Coke vs. Pepsi

For years, Pepsi's plan to win the cola wars depended on **diversification**, or being involved in many things. Pepsi figured that people who drank cola also ate in fast-food restaurants and bought lots of snack foods. Therefore, Pepsi thought, food businesses could boost Pepsi's business. For example, if you went to a restaurant that Pepsi owned, such as Pizza Hut, you could only buy a Pepsi. Pepsi's idea was to connect eating with drinking Pepsi.

Coke's strategy was different. Coke didn't want any distractions. The company decided to spend its time on its **core**, or most important, business—selling drinks. Coke was afraid that if its employees had to spend time making pizza and operating restaurants, their focus on Coke might slip. So the company spent all its energy on beverages.

The Verdict

So, two competing companies have different ideas about how to sell pretty much the same product. It's an interesting race. So far, Coke is the clear winner. By concentrating on its core business, the company has done very well. Its stock is up, and it has about 44 percent of the soft-drink market.

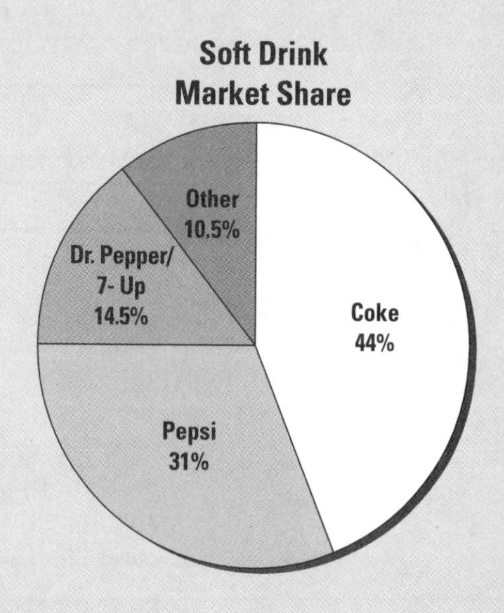

Pepsi has not done as well. Its market share is about 31 percent. In 1997, Pepsi seemed to realize that the fast-food restaurants it owned were not helping it succeed. That year, Pepsi sold its Pizza Hut, Taco Bell, and KFC restaurants.

Pepsi certainly hasn't given up. Coke admits that. Coke's Ivester said the cola war will probably continue for decades. "This is not the last couple of years, or the last couple of months. It's years and years and years," he said.

Pepsi's first attack after selling its restaurants was to introduce Storm. Storm is a lemon-lime drink that is like 7-Up or Sprite. Pepsi wants to take over that market.

Pepsi's next move was to file a lawsuit against Coke. Pepsi's suit says that Coke forces the people who buy its fountain drinks to sell only Coke products. Fountain drinks are sold at restaurants and movie theaters. That is illegal, Pepsi says. This series of moves by Pepsi shows that Ivester is right. Anyone who gets involved in the cola war is likely to be fighting for a very long time.

Review your PACA chart. Make notes beside the supporting information you added to be sure you will remember what you've learned. These notes will help you review your understanding of your reading.

Apply It............ To check your understanding of the selection, circle the best answer to each of the following questions.

1. Pepsi's first strategy to beat Coke was to
   a. shut Coke out of the restaurant market.
   b. start businesses that would help each other succeed.
   c. concentrate on its soft-drink business.
   d. try to keep Coke in court.
2. The word *core* in the "Coke *vs.* Pepsi" section means
   a. the center.
   b. the best-known.
   c. the most interesting.
   d. the most important.
3. You can infer that when Pepsi sold its restaurants,
   a. it gave up the soft-drink business there too.
   b. it was winning the cola war.
   c. it was admitting that the Pepsi strategy hadn't worked.
   d. Coke wanted to buy them.
4. Ivester thinks that the cola war will continue because
   a. he wants it to.
   b. it is good for business.
   c. Pepsi still has a large share of the market and isn't giving up.
   d. the government will not allow one company to win.

Test Tip

When you compare and contrast two things, you look at their similarities (compare) and at their differences (contrast).

Use the lines below to write your answers for numbers 5 and 6. Use your PACA chart and the pie chart to help you.

5. Compare and contrast Coke's and Pepsi's approaches to the cola war.

____

____

____

6. Imagine you have been hired by Pepsi to increase sales. What would you suggest? Use examples and reasons to back up your suggestions.

____

____

____

Unit 3 Review

Reading in Social Studies

In this unit, you have practiced using the KWL Plus, Outlining, PACA, and PLAN reading strategies. Choose one strategy and use it when you read the selection below. Use a separate sheet of paper to draw charts, take notes, and summarize what you learn.

Hint *Remember that all reading strategies have activities for before, during, and after reading. To review these steps, look back at Unit 1 or at the last page of this book.*

America's Most Famous Traitor

Benedict Arnold became famous for betraying his country. His name came to mean "traitor." At the start of the Revolutionary War, though, Benedict Arnold was a hero. Why did he betray his country?

Benedict Arnold was born in Connecticut. His family was well respected. During the French and Indian War, from 1754 to 1763, he fought in the colonial army.

After his father died, in 1761, Arnold moved back home. He became a druggist and bookseller. In 1775, as the American colonies prepared to fight for independence, Arnold was elected captain of an army unit.

Arnold was in the middle of the fight for independence from the start. He helped lead the charge to take Fort Ticonderoga from the British in 1775. George Washington's troops were able to use the supplies from that fort to stay alive. That same year, Arnold led a charge on British Quebec. The attack failed. Even so, Arnold was promoted to brigadier general.

In 1777, Benedict Arnold led the attack in the Battle of Ridgefield, Connecticut. He gained fame for his courage. Then Arnold became commander of Philadelphia in 1778. There he met Margaret Shippen. They soon married. The couple spent money freely.

Next, Arnold became head of West Point, a critical post. West Point protected the Hudson Valley.

Then Arnold did something no one expected. He offered to give West Point to the British for money.

On the night of September 23, 1780, three colonial soldiers captured a British major named John Andre. He was carrying papers that told of Arnold's plot. Andre was hanged as a spy. Arnold learned of Andre's capture and fled to a British warship in the Hudson River. The British made him an officer in their army.

The Trail of the Traitor

Why did Benedict Arnold do it? One reason was money. Arnold and

his wife did not have the money to support their rich tastes. Also, Arnold was angry because younger officers were promoted above him.

The army in Philadelphia also claimed that Arnold ignored military law. Those charges made him furious. All these factors built up. Finally, Arnold decided to betray his country.

After his escape, Arnold fought against the colonies. In his home state, Connecticut, Arnold burned more than 150 buildings. His British troops killed colonial soldiers.

Finally, in 1781, Arnold and his family left America for Britain. The British saw him as a traitor. If he would betray his country once, they thought, he would do it again.

Arnold was less successful in business in England than he had been in the colonies. The deal he had made was more costly than he had expected.

Use your notes and charts to help you answer the questions below.

1. Which of the following did Benedict Arnold do?
   a. He helped George Washington lead the army.
   b. He hanged John Andre.
   c. He betrayed his country to the British.
   d. He became a respected British citizen.
2. Why was West Point important in the Revolutionary War?
   a. It was an important center for communications.
   b. It protected the Hudson Valley.
   c. It was the training ground for colonial officers.
   d. It was the British headquarters.
3. Arnold was distrusted by the British because
   a. they considered him to be an American at heart.
   b. they didn't trust someone who had betrayed his country.
   c. he was not useful to the British once he left America.
   d. he never became a British citizen.
4. Why was Andre's capture important to the colonial forces?

___

___

5. Why did Benedict Arnold betray his country?

___

___

Unit 4
Reading in Science

You probably read more science-related texts than you think you do. Besides your textbooks in school, you may read newspaper articles about how wolves are vanishing or how new medicines are saving lives. When you put together a music system, you are using your knowledge of step-by-step processes. Learning how to read scientific or technical information can help you not just in class but also in everyday life.

How Science Reading Is Organized

In contrast to some other subjects, science often depends on knowledge that builds on itself. You need to understand one idea before you can move to the next. That makes reading science a careful process. You can't skip words you don't understand. Often you can't figure out the meaning from context. To get the most out of science reading, you need to read with concentration. Knowing the way the text is organized can help. When you recognize the pattern of a text, you can more easily fit the facts you learn into a larger picture. Here are some text patterns you may see in science reading.

Steps of a Process. Science reading often focuses on understanding a process. Science texts describe how living and nonliving things change and develop. For example, a biology text may explain the life cycle of a butterfly. A lab manual may describe the steps that are needed to complete an experiment. When you see this pattern, you know to look for the next step as you read. Diagrams are a common part of this structure. Watch for them, too. Below is a drawing of how an article that describes a process might be organized:

Water Cycle

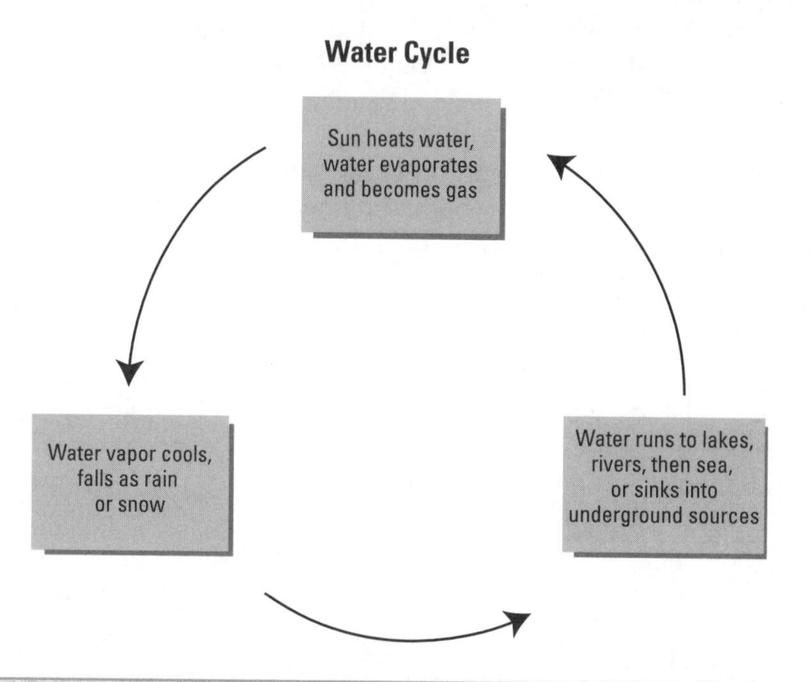

Main Idea and Details. A science reading that discusses a subject may be organized in this way. There is a main topic supported by major points and evidence. You may find this pattern in any of the sciences. Much of science is classification, and that is a common pattern here. For example, a life science text may discuss the types of biomes. Below is a wheel-and-spoke diagram of how this type of organization might look.

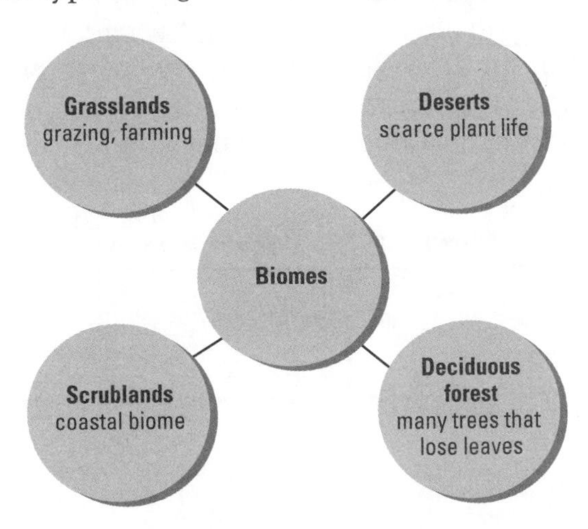

Cause and Effect. Science reading may contain a series of causes and effects. You may see this kind of description when a reading discusses how humans have affected Earth. Also, causes and effects can explain topics such as why glaciers form. Creating a diagram that shows causes and effects can help you understand how these events can work together to form a chain.

Acid Rain

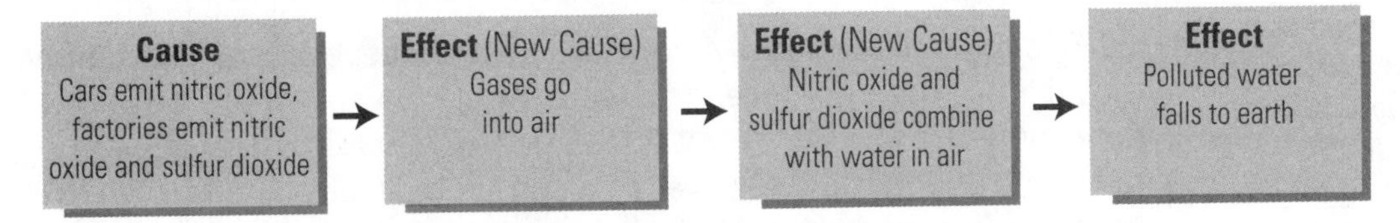

Getting the Most from Your Reading

If you can recognize the way a reading is organized, you will be better able to understand what you read. You will be able to think about what kind of information might be next and how all the points in the reading fit together. Drawing diagrams like the ones on these two pages can show you these patterns. Thinking about how a reading is organized can help you understand—and remember—what you read.

Lesson 13 Earth Science: Killer Waves

Understand It...... This selection is about dangerous waves called *tsunamis*. You will read about what happens as a tsunami approaches—and then strikes—land. The KWL Plus strategy is a good one to use with this selection because you probably have read or heard about tsunamis or about the earthquakes that can cause them. You can use what you already know to help you learn more about tsunamis.

Hint
You can review the KWL Plus strategy on page 4.

Try It.............. Draw a KWL chart like the one below on a separate sheet of paper. Think about what you already know about waves and tsunamis and write that information in the K column. Write what you want to find out about this topic in the W column. Look for answers to your questions as you read. After you finish reading, write what you learned in the L column.

Strategy Tip
Be sure that some of your W questions ask *why* or *how*.

K (What I know)	W (What I want to know)	L (What I've learned)

Vocabulary Tip
Certain words are set in boldface, or dark, type. These words are often vocabulary words or key terms in the selection. Usually, a sentence that contains a boldface word also has a definition nearby.

Killer Waves

Ocean waves can be lots of fun. You may have been tossed about or hitched a ride to shore on a big wave. You may have seen others enjoying an ocean swim or surfing in a movie or on TV.

Not all waves are fun, though. Some can destroy beaches and damage property. They can even kill. These killer waves are called **tsunamis**.

A tsunami (tsoo-NAHM-ee) is a series of ocean waves. A tsunami moves from the open ocean toward the shore. The depth of the water determines its speed. Far out in the ocean, where the water is very deep, a tsunami moves as fast as a commercial jet plane. Traveling at nearly 600 miles (965 km) per hour, it rapidly moves toward land. When the tsunami reaches shallow water along a coastline, it slows down. However, as its speed drops, its height increases. By the time the tsunami hits land, waves might be as high as 100 feet (30 m).

Striking Land

A tsunami strikes land as a series of breaking waves. The first wave is usually not the largest. The waves that follow tend to increase in force and size. Sand is swept from the beach. Plants and even trees are uprooted. A fast-moving wall of water moves inland, destroying everything in its path.

Strategy Tip
This paragraph describes some causes of tsunamis. Add this information to the W section of your KWL chart.

Strategy Tip
What does the photograph tell you about the destructive power of tsunamis? You might add some questions to the W section of your KWL chart.

Tsunamis have nearly destroyed a number of coastal communities. In 1964, an earthquake occurred in the Pacific Ocean that produced a tsunami. Deadly waves struck the coasts of Alaska, Oregon, and California. Wharves, buildings, even sawmills broke apart. The tsunami caused more than $106 million in property damage. More than 100 people died.

The Earthquake Connection

A tsunami forms when something suddenly causes a major disturbance in a body of water. A landslide, a volcanic eruption, an explosion, or the impact of a meteorite can trigger a tsunami. However, the most common cause of the killer waves is an earthquake under the sea floor.

Tsunami damage on an island off Japan

Most earthquakes occur along a fault line. A fault is a break in the Earth's crust, where movement can occur. Usually, the rocks on both sides of a fault are squeezed together very tightly. They might not move for thousands of years. Over time, pressure on the rocks increases. When the pressure becomes too great, the rocks move. Sometimes, one large area of rock slips under another area. If that happens on the ocean floor, it disturbs a huge amount of water. The displaced water forms waves. A tsunami is born.

Tsunami Warning System

People cannot stop tsunamis from forming. However, they can take steps to protect lives and property from a tsunami's deadly force. The key is advance warning. Currently, two tsunami warning centers are in operation. The Alaska Tsunami Warning Center monitors the coasts of Alaska, British Columbia, Washington, Oregon, and California. The Pacific Tsunami Warning Center monitors Hawaii and the Pacific Ocean.

Each center watches for earthquakes under the sea floor. When an earthquake occurs, the center issues a tsunami warning. Coastal communities most likely to be affected receive the warning. Local authorities know the approximate time a tsunami might strike. Evacuation plans are set in motion. People move to higher ground. Lives are spared.

Now look back at your W questions. See whether they were answered. You might want to reread if you think the answers to your questions are in the selection. Next, fill in the L column. Then use your KWL chart to help you write a summary of the article. Your summary and your chart can also help you answer the questions on the next page.

Earth Science: Killer Waves

Apply It............ To check your understanding of the selection, circle the best answer to each of the following questions.

1. The main idea of this selection is that
   a. tsunamis always occur before earthquakes.
   b. ocean waves can be dangerous.
   c. a tsunami is a deadly force of nature.
   d. Alaska has many earthquakes.

2. Which of the following do *not* cause tsunamis?
   a. falling meteorites
   b. hurricanes
   c. volcanic eruptions
   d. landslides

Test Tip

The choices in question 3 may seem confusing because they are so much alike. Break each choice into two pieces. For example, in choice *a*, ask yourself what happens when the water depth increases. Does the wave speed increase? Test each choice before you decide on one.

3. Which sentence describes how water depth affects the speed of a tsunami?
   a. As water depth increases, wave speed stays the same.
   b. As water depth decreases, wave speed increases.
   c. As water depth increases, wave speed decreases.
   d. As water depth decreases, wave speed decreases.

4. What is the best way to protect people from tsunamis?
   a. Don't let people live in coastal areas.
   b. Teach children how to swim in the ocean.
   c. Provide early warning.
   d. Build high walls along beaches.

Use the lines below to write your answers for numbers 5 and 6. You can use your KWL chart to help you.

5. Explain the relationship between an earthquake and a tsunami.

____

____

____

____

Test Tip

Question 6 asks what *you* would do. When you answer the question, include the facts from the selection that helped you decide what to do.

6. Imagine that your parents have just found their "dream house." It is beautiful and low-priced. However, it was built in an area that has been struck by tsunamis. Should they buy the house? Why or why not?

____

____

____

____

Lesson 14 Life Science: Light! Lens! Vision!

Understand It...... Have you ever heard the expression "A picture is worth a thousand words"? According to researchers, that saying has a lot of truth. They have found that pictures or other visual images help some learners understand new information. The PLAN strategy gives you a system for creating your own "picture" as you read.

Hint

You can review the PLAN strategy on page 16.

Try It.............. Many science articles describe relationships. The PLAN strategy can help you see these relationships. Think about the kind of word map you want to try. Since the article discusses one subject—vision problems—you might want to try a wheel-and-spoke diagram. Predict the kinds of vision problems people have and the solutions to those problems.

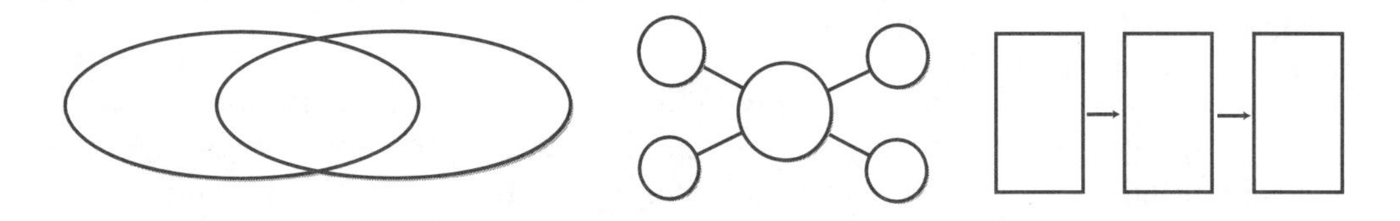

Strategy Tip

Pay close attention to any diagrams that appear with a selection. They may help you "see" what the text is describing.

Strategy Tip

Don't forget to read captions and labels about art or pictures. They often give you more information you want to remember.

Light! Lens! Vision!

As you read, your eyes work so that you see the words on this page. You see an object when light enters your eye through the pupil. The light moves through the pupil to a lens. Muscles attached to the lens cause the lens to change shape. That focuses the light to form an image on the retina. The retina responds to the light by creating nerve signals. The optic nerve carries these signals to the brain. The brain then interprets the signals. It tells you what you are seeing. All of this happens automatically, without your even thinking about it.

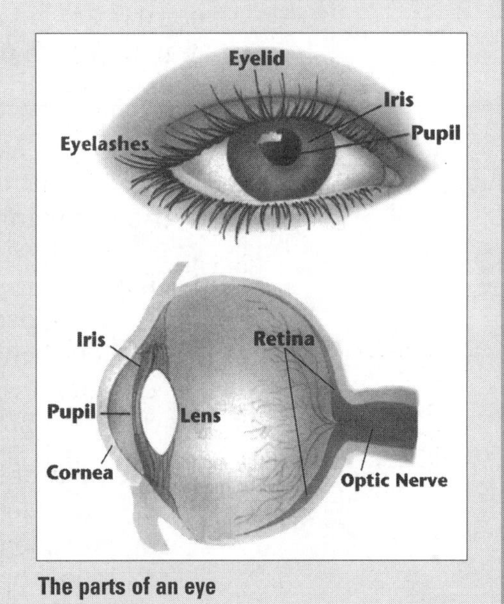

The parts of an eye

Most people are born with good eyesight. The lenses in their eyes change shape quickly and keep objects in focus. However, some people cannot see objects clearly. The muscles in their eyes don't allow the lenses to change shape enough to focus images properly.

One common vision problem is myopia, or nearsightedness. Nearsighted people can see nearby objects clearly, but distant objects look blurry. That happens because the eye's lens focuses an image in front of the retina rather than on it.

A concave lens can correct nearsightedness. It looks like a shallow bowl when you see it from the side. Concave lenses bend light outward before it enters the eye. The light then bends a second time as it passes through the natural lens. Bending the light twice helps focus a clear image on the retina.

Vocabulary Tip

When you find an unknown word, look at the other words in the sentence. Sometimes, they provide clues to the meaning of the new term. Use this tip to determine the meaning of *hypermetropia*.

Another common vision problem is **hypermetropia**, or farsightedness. Farsighted people can see distant objects clearly, but nearby objects look blurry. That happens when the distance between the front and back of the eye is very short. The eye's lens cannot focus incoming light.

A convex lens can correct farsightedness. It looks like the outside edge of a circle. The lens bends light inward. As the light moves through the eye, the natural lens bends it again. This focuses a clear image on the retina.

Corrective lenses can be either eyeglasses or contact lenses. Eyeglasses contain corrective lenses held by a frame. Contact lenses are tiny plastic disks worn directly on the surface of the eye. Millions of people worldwide wear eyeglasses or contact lenses to correct their vision problems.

When you finish reading, look at your word map. Does it contain the article's main points? Does it contain information that supports these points? Reread and add information. Then make some notes to help you remember what you have read. You can do that with a summary, an oral review, or a list—use the review process that works best for you.

Apply It........... To check your understanding of the article, circle the best answer to each of the following questions.

1. The main idea of this article is that
   a. many people wear eyeglasses.
   b. light bends as it moves through a lens.
   c. certain vision problems can be corrected with special lenses.
   d. vision problems are a result of aging.

2. The parts of the eye through which light passes, in order from first to last, are
   a. retina, lens, pupil.
   b. pupil, lens, optic nerve.
   c. retina, optic nerve, lens.
   d. pupil, lens, retina.

3. Which of the following states a fact about farsightedness?
   a. Farsightedness can be corrected with a convex lens.
   b. Farsightedness is easier to deal with than nearsightedness.
   c. Farsightedness is more troublesome to senior citizens than to children.
   d. Most farsighted people enjoy wearing contact lenses.

Test Tip

Question 4 asks you to *infer* an answer to a question. Think about what you learned about nearsightedness. Then read the answer choices. Based on what you've learned, which choice seems to be the most reasonable one?

4. What can you infer about a nearsighted person who is not wearing corrective lenses?
   a. He or she will have difficulty reading the words on this page.
   b. The numbers on a bank statement will be blurry.
   c. If the person is seated in the last row of a theater, words flashed across a movie screen will appear blurry.
   d. He or she should not wear corrective lenses while driving.

5. How is the retina of the eye like a movie screen?
   a. Light passes through each item.
   b. Images are formed on each item.
   c. Each item can create nerve signals.
   d. Each item can focus light.

Use the lines below to write your answers for numbers 6 and 7. You can use your PLAN notes to help you.

6. Explain the difference between a concave lens and a convex lens. You might want to draw a picture to illustrate your explanation.

____

____

____

____

____

7. Explain the effect of lens shape on passing light.

____

____

____

____

____

Lesson 15 Earth Science: Myths and Planets

Understand It..... Science texts often describe how things are connected. Using the PLAN strategy can help you "see" these connections. Predict the kind of information you will read in the text. First look at the title. It states the topic. Then preview the selection. Focus on key words or phrases that are repeated. Don't forget to look at any pictures or diagrams that accompany the article. They usually highlight important points.

Hint

You can review the PLAN strategy on page 16.

Try It.............. Choose a graphic for your word map. You can copy one of the graphics below onto another sheet of paper. You can also create your own graphic. Write check marks next to information you know about. Write question marks next to information you don't know about. As you read the article, locate important information. After reading, add notes to your graphic that will help you remember that information.

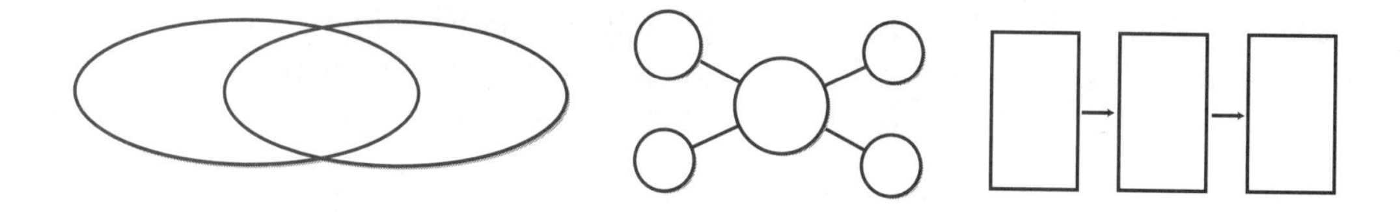

Strategy Tip

To find important information, read the topic sentence of each paragraph. These sentences give you clues to the main points of the article.

Myths and Planets

The world around you changes constantly. The sun rises and sets. The moon seems to change shape in a regular cycle. Tides rise and fall; seasons come and go. Modern science helps people understand why these changes occur. People who lived long ago did not know about scientific explanations. To make sense of what they saw, they created stories called myths. The myths described how gods and goddesses caused changes in the natural world.

There are as many kinds of myths as there are cultures. People from ancient times, such as the Greeks, Egyptians, Celts, and Norse, created myths. Early Romans wrote stories to explain natural events too. Hundreds of years later, modern scientists used the Roman myths to name some of the planets. They identified some traits of each planet. Then they looked for a figure in mythology who looked and acted in the same way. They named the planet for that figure.

The planet Mercury was named for the Roman messenger of the gods. According to mythology, Mercury wore sandals with wings. This footwear allowed him to cover great distances very quickly. To deliver his messages successfully, Mercury needed to be quite crafty. The messenger relied on tricks to avoid danger.

The traits of this mythological figure match those of the planet closest to the sun. Mercury orbits the sun faster than any other planet.

Because Mercury is small and close to the sun, the planet is hard to see from Earth. At some points in its orbit, Mercury appears low in the western sky. At other times, people can see it in the eastern sky. For these reasons, the planet was named after the fast, tricky Roman messenger.

The fifth planet from the sun was also named for a mythological figure. In Roman mythology, Jupiter ruled all the gods. He was considered the king of the universe. Because it is the largest planet in our solar system, Jupiter was named for the greatest of the gods. The largest of Jupiter's moons, Ganymede, is named for a character from Greek mythology. Ganymede served as cupbearer to the gods.

Vocabulary Tip

Sometimes information is not directly stated. It is implied. This paragraph implies—but does not directly state—the name of the Roman god of the sea. What is the name of the god?

The names of the other planets can be traced to Roman myths, too. From Earth, Neptune looks blue. For that reason, the planet was named after the Roman god of the sea. Mars looks reddish in color. It was named for the Roman god of bloodshed and war. Pluto lies farthest from the sun. Its orbit takes it to the outer edge of the solar system. The planet was named for the Roman god of the underworld.

Someday, scientists might need to agree on a name for a new planet. Advances in technology constantly produce new tools for looking at the universe. Scientists use them to gather information about distant parts of the solar system. Perhaps an unknown planet orbits somewhere far out in space. If so, the planet will need a name. Scientists could decide to continue the pattern and name the heavenly body after a character from mythology.

What did you learn about the naming of the planets that you didn't predict? Add that information to your word map. Then be sure to add notes to your map to help you remember what you've learned.

Apply It

To check your understanding of the article, circle the best answer to each of the following questions.

1. The main idea of this article is that
   a. everyone enjoys reading myths.
   b. ancient people did not explore nature.
   c. many planets were named for mythological figures.
   d. the Romans had the most interesting mythological figures.

2. People living in ancient times created myths
   a. to record family information.
   b. to explain the natural world.
   c. for entertainment.
   d. to develop children's reading skills.

3. The Roman god of war was
   a. Pluto.
   b. Saturn.
   c. Mercury.
   d. Mars.

Test Tip

Review the difference between a fact and an opinion. A fact is something that can be proven to be true or false. An opinion is a person's judgment about an issue.

4. Which of the following statements is an opinion?
   a. Naming planets after mythological figures was a good idea.
   b. All the known planets in our solar system have been named.
   c. The planet closest to the sun moves quickly.
   d. Technology gives scientists new tools for investigation.

5. The writer's tone can best be described as
   a. angry.
   b. informative.
   c. mysterious.
   d. humorous.

Use the lines below to write your answers for numbers 6 and 7. You can use your PLAN notes to help you.

6. Why do you think people who lived long ago created a myth to explain the cause of thunder and lightning?

7. Identify a change that occurs in nature. Write a myth that describes a possible cause of the change. Look back at the first paragraph of the text for some ideas.

Lesson 16 Life Science: Eating for the Big Contest

Understand It...... An outline can show you how the parts of an article relate to one another. Outlining is especially helpful for science articles because it can give you a framework for the reading. It can help you see how the different pieces of information are connected.

Hint

You can review the outlining strategy on page 8.

Try It.............. Look at the title and preview the selection. Look for clues about the main idea. Look at the title and subheadings. They tell you about the kinds of information that the selection contains. They also show how the information is arranged. These headings show you that food is fuel for the body and that athletes need a balanced diet to do well.

First, read the article carefully. Then make your outline. Use Roman numerals to show major ideas, capital letters to show major points, and numbers to show supporting evidence. Be sure that the structure of your outline matches the structure of the selection.

I. ______________________
  A. ______________________
  B. ______________________
    1. ______________________
    2. ______________________
II. ______________________
  A. ______________________
  B. ______________________
    1. ______________________
    2. ______________________

Strategy Tip

The title of the selection can also be the title of your outline. You might want to write the selection's subheadings on the lines that have Roman numerals.

Eating for the Big Contest

The human body is like a machine. It needs fuel to do work. Nutrients are fuel for the body. They are chemical substances in foods that the body needs for growth and energy. The body uses nutrients to carry out life processes.

A Balanced Diet

There are five kinds of nutrients—carbohydrates, fats, proteins, vitamins, and minerals. Some foods are rich in one nutrient. Most foods contain many nutrients.

The body needs different amounts of each type of nutrient daily. Eating a balanced diet fuels the body with those nutrients. The Food Pyramid Guide can help people plan a balanced diet. It shows the kinds of foods and number of servings a person should eat every day.

Life Science: Eating for the Big Contest

Strategy Tip

Illustrations in science articles often explain the text. Look at the drawings and read the labels. You can use this information in your outline.

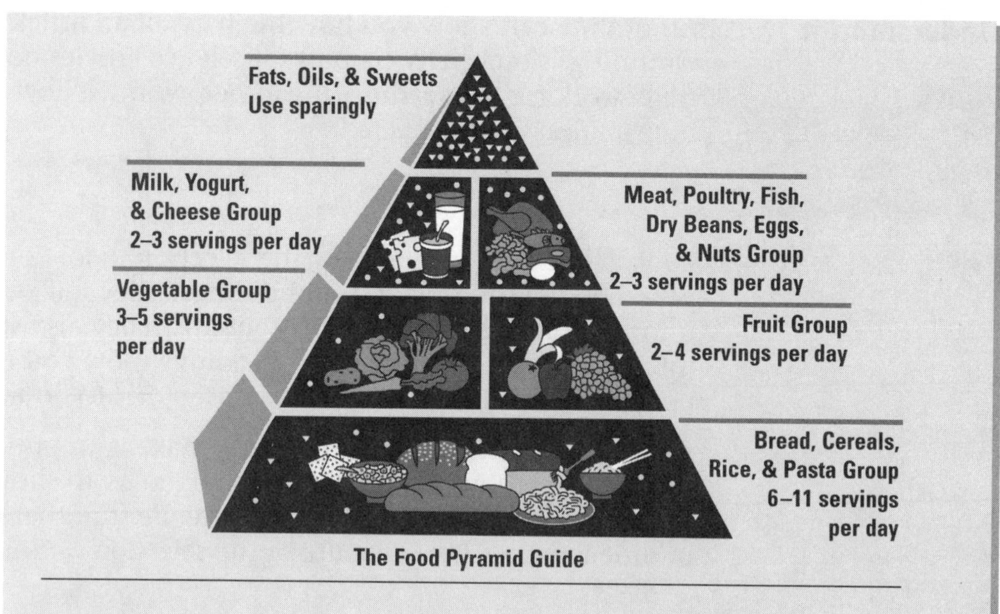

The Food Pyramid Guide

Fuel for Athletes

A balanced diet is especially important to athletes. Athletic activities are hard work. An athlete's body burns fuel rapidly. It requires a greater supply of fuel than does a person who is not an athlete. Eating healthful foods increases an athlete's power and endurance. Healthful eating helps an athlete manage weight and fend off injuries.

Most nutrition experts say that an athlete's diet should be high in carbohydrates. Carbohydrates are nutrients that supply the body with energy. They also help build muscle. Starches such as bread and pasta are carbohydrates. They fuel the body with energy over a long period of time. Sixty to 70 percent of the food an athlete eats should be high in carbohydrates.

Water is also important to athletes. More than two-thirds of the human body is made up of water. People lose some of that liquid when they sweat. Athletes must replace the lost fluid. Drinking a liter of water before each competition helps maintain the necessary water balance.

The Pregame Meal

Regardless of the sport, every athlete should eat a meal three or four hours before competing. Fueling the body on carbohydrates, such as cereal, bread, and pasta, is important. The meal should include fruits and vegetables too. They supply the body with important minerals and add carbohydrates. Athletes should avoid sugary foods, such as candy and soft drinks. Although they can give a quick energy "boost," these foods also cause a **subsequent** energy "drop." Most important, an athlete should drink two to three cups of caffeine-free fluids. A balanced pregame meal helps an athlete reach peak performance.

Vocabulary Tip

When you find an unknown word, look at the other words in the sentence. Sometimes they provide clues to the meaning of the new word. Use this tip to find the meaning of *subsequent*.

Now review your outline. Does it mention all of the major points in the selection? Does it show you the details that support these points? If it doesn't, reread the selection and fill in the missing parts of the outline.

Apply It............ To check your understanding of the selection, circle the best answer to each question below.

1. How is the human body like a car?
   a. Both do work.
   b. Both need fuel.
   c. Both take in carbohydrates.
   d. Both do work *and* need fuel.

Test Tip

The word *except* shows that three of the choices are alike in some way. The correct answer is the choice that is different from the others.

2. All the following substances are nutrients *except*
   a. water.
   b. proteins.
   c. fats.
   d. carbohydrates.

3. How do the food groups in the Food Pyramid Guide relate to one another?
   a. People should eat more servings of the higher groups in the pyramid.
   b. The lower groups in the pyramid have the greatest value to the body.
   c. The higher groups in the pyramid have the greatest value to the body.
   d. People should eat fewer servings of the lower groups in the pyramid.

4. In the "Fuel for Athletes" section, to *fend off* injuries means
   a. to suffer many injuries.
   b. to lose strength.
   c. to avoid being hurt.
   d. to increase energy.

5. Which of the following foods should *not* be included in a pregame meal?
   a. a cup of coffee
   b. whole-wheat toast
   c. fruit salad
   d. pasta

Use the lines below to write your answers for numbers 6 and 7. You can use your outline to help you.

6. Explain why many runners eat a bowl of pasta before a race.

___

___

7. Use the Food Pyramid Guide to create a menu for tomorrow's breakfast, lunch, and dinner. Be sure to follow the recommended servings.

___

___

Lesson 17 Life Science: Do Animals Have Emotions?

Understand It...... If you are a pet owner, you may have thought about the question in the title. You can probably make predictions about ideas that might be in the article. The PACA strategy will help you make your predictions. It is a good strategy to use when you have some information about a topic. It can help you attach new information to what you already know.

Hint
You can review the PACA strategy on page 12.

Try It.............. Look at the title and the subheadings. You can see that the article will probably tell you about two points of view. Now preview the article. What kind of information do you think it contains?

Draw a chart like the one below on a separate sheet of paper. Write your predictions in the Predictions column. As you read, look for statements that confirm your predictions. Add a check mark in the small box of any prediction you confirm. Revise or add to your predictions after you read. If you find new information, write it and add a star to the small box. Note any support you find for your predictions in the Support column.

Strategy Tip
Do you think animals have emotions? Do you think the author feels the way you do? Form some predictions from these questions.

Predictions	Support

Strategy Tip
After you read the first paragraph, think about the author's ideas. Do you think the author believes that animals have emotions or not? If you need to, add to or revise your predictions on your PACA chart.

Do Animals Have Emotions?

In the summer of 1996, a three-year-old boy fell 20 feet into a gorilla exhibit. Horrified bystanders at the Chicago Zoo watched as an eight-year-old female gorilla moved toward the boy. With her own youngster clinging to her back, the female scooped up the boy. She cradled the boy in her lap. She even patted him gently on the back. Finally, the gorilla set the boy down near one of the exhibit doorways.

The gorilla's actions stunned the crowd. However, scientists who study animal behavior were not shocked at all. They saw just another example of the maternal instinct of gorillas. The scientists believe the gorilla saw the boy as another infant. She acted like the child's mother. According to scientists, she simply followed her instinct.

Other people disagree. They argue that the gorilla's actions showed she felt sympathy for the boy. They believe that her feelings for the youngster caused her to rescue him. Those people feel that emotion triggered the gorilla's actions.

Can an animal experience the kinds of emotions people feel? People have asked that question for hundreds of years.

Vocabulary Tip

Find the sentence that contains the word *sonar*. Look at the sentence that follows it for a clue about the meaning of the word.

The Scientific View

To the scientific world, survival guides animals' actions. Animals behave in certain ways so they can stay alive. Behaviors that animals are born with are called instincts. For example, nest-building is an instinct in certain birds. Young birds do not have to be shown how to build a nest. They simply know how to do it. Other animal behaviors are responses to a stimulus. For example, bats use **sonar** to gain information about their surroundings. Reflected sound waves tell bats where to find prey. The sound waves are a stimulus. Bats respond to the stimulus.

The scientist Charles Darwin explored the possibility that animals have emotions. In 1873, he published a book called *The Expression of the Emotions in Man and Animals*. Darwin believed that some kinds of animals have a system of emotional expression like that of humans. He used that connection to link humans and animals.

Pet Owners

Millions of pet owners believe that their pets share such human emotions as love, joy, fear, shame, and sorrow. Their relationship with their pets is based on giving and receiving these emotions.

Dog owners often describe times when their pet showed feelings. A dog that hides under a bed during a thunderstorm shows fear. A puppy that jumps on a young child returning home from school shows joy. A dog that puts its tail between its legs as it is scolded shows shame.

Then there is the tale of Bobby, a shaggy dog in Scotland. After Bobby's owner died, the dog watched the burial. Every night for the next 14 years, the dog went back to the graveyard and slept on his master's grave.

Can such behavior be explained by instinct? Was Bobby responding to a stimulus? Or was Bobby showing sorrow? What do you think?

What did you learn in this article about animals and emotions? Add these points to your list of predictions. You can also revise any predictions that were wrong. Be sure that you've added support for each of your predictions in the right column. This support will help you understand and remember the article.

Apply It............ To check your understanding of the article, circle the best answer to each of the following questions.

1. Some people feel the gorilla's actions toward the boy showed she
   - **a.** was angry that the boy came into her exhibit.
   - **b.** hoped the boy would play with her own youngster.
   - **c.** cared about the young boy.
   - **d.** loved her own child.

Test Tip

Read the questions carefully. For question 2, several choices may be true, but only one choice states the *main idea* of the article.

2. The main idea of this selection is that
   a. all living things have needs.
   b. animals may have humanlike emotions.
   c. humans respond to stimuli as animals do.
   d. Charles Darwin believed that animals lack emotions.

3. Nest-building is an example of
   a. an instinct.
   b. a behavior.
   c. a response.
   d. an instinct and a behavior.

4. Sonar is
   a. a type of emotion.
   b. a way of detecting reflected sound waves.
   c. a response to a stimulus.
   d. a type of bat.

5. What can you infer about the author's ideas about animal emotions?
   a. The author believes that animals don't have emotions.
   b. The author believes that animals may have emotions.
   c. The author doesn't state an opinion on the subject.
   d. The author doesn't believe that animals can think.

Use the lines below to write your answers for numbers 6 and 7. You can use your PACA notes to help you.

6. Write a paragraph comparing the scientific view of animal emotions with that of pet owners.

____

____

____

____

7. Do you think animals have emotions? Give evidence that supports your position.

____

____

____

____

Lesson 18 Lab Activity: Using a Microscope

Understand It......

Good detectives use evidence to solve crimes. Often, the evidence can't be seen without a microscope. Scientists in a crime lab examine the items to find clues that will solve cases. You also need to develop your microscope skills to do well in science. Many lab activities call for microscope use. Successfully completing those activities depends on knowing how to use a microscope.

Hint

You can review the PLAN strategy on page 16.

Try It..............

This selection describes how to use a microscope. Using the PLAN strategy can help you understand the directions for performing a lab investigation. You'll notice when you preview the selection that it lists things to do in order. Because the selection is organized in this way, you might want to use the sequence chart pictured below, at the right.

Copy this graphic or another one that you choose onto another sheet of paper. Write the title of each procedure section in a new box. Leave room in the box to write notes on the sections. Write check marks next to information you know about. Write question marks next to information you don't know about. After you read the article, make notes on the steps in each procedure section. Then add notes that will help you remember that information.

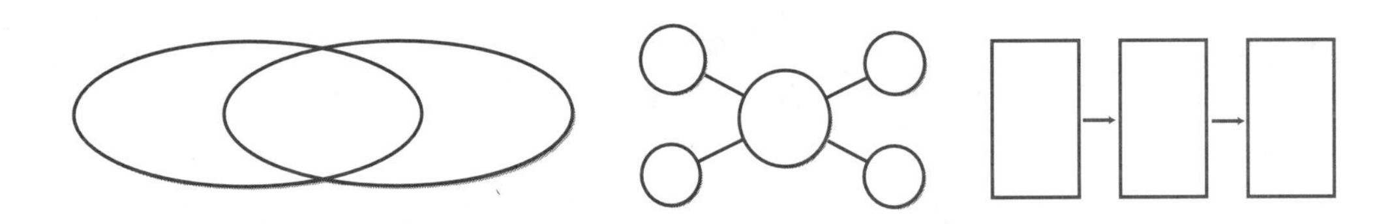

Strategy Tip

When you preview the selection, you'll see that there are a lot of subheadings. The subheadings will help you predict what you will do in this lab activity.

Using a Microscope

Background Information

A compound microscope has two or more lenses. The lens at the top of the microscope tube is the ocular lens. The lens in each objective, or cylinder, is an objective lens. Some microscopes have three or four objective lenses. Both the ocular and objective lenses magnify images.

Materials

compound microscope	dropper	microscope slide
water	cover slip	newspaper
lens paper	scissors	

Procedure

a. **Preparing the Slide**

1. Clean the microscope slide and cover slip with the lens paper. Be gentle; slides and cover slips break easily. Once they are clean, be careful not to get fingerprints on them.

Vocabulary Tip

Notice that the letter *e* is in italic, or slanted, type. This style of type makes words or symbols stand out. Here it shows you that you are looking at a letter, not at a word.

Strategy Tip

You might want to add notes in each box of your diagram that describe the steps in each Procedure section.

2. Use the dropper to put one drop of water on the slide.
3. Find a letter ***e*** in the newspaper. Cut it out. Place it over the drop of water on the slide. Slowly lower the cover slip over the *e*. The *e* is your specimen.
4. Place the slide on the microscope stage. Use the clips to hold the slide in place.

b. Focusing the Microscope

1. Look through the eyepiece of the microscope. Turn the coarse adjustment knob until the *e* is in focus. It will still be a little blurry.
2. Now turn the fine adjustment knob. Look through the eyepiece. Turn the knob until the *e* is clearly in focus.

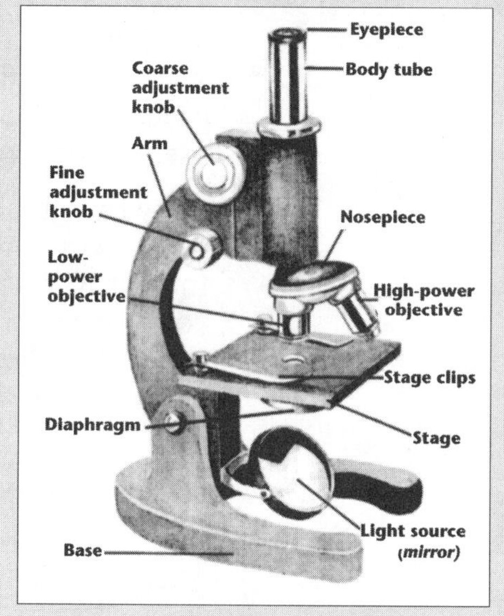

The parts of a microscope

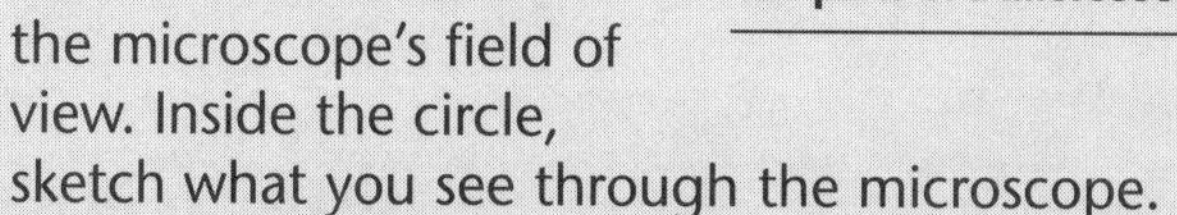

c. Observations

1. On a sheet of paper, draw a circle that shows the microscope's field of view. Inside the circle, sketch what you see through the microscope.
2. Does the letter *e* look different when viewed under the microscope? If so, in what way is it different?

d. Conclusions

1. What parts of the microscope focus an image?
2. Do you think that all compound microscopes are basically the same? Explain your answer.

Now look at your PLAN graphic. It should remind you of how to use a microscope properly. Could you use it to help you complete an experiment? If not, go back and add notes that make the steps clear. You can use your chart to help you answer the questions on the next page.

Apply It. . . . . To check your understanding of the selection, circle the best answer to each question below.

1. What do both ocular and objective lenses do?
   - a. They clean the slides.
   - b. They hold specimens in place.
   - c. They adjust the focus.
   - d. They magnify images.
2. A *specimen* is
   - a. the lens of a microscope.
   - b. an item used to clean a microscope.
   - c. a person using a microscope.
   - d. an item being viewed through a microscope.
3. What must you do immediately after placing the cover slip over the *e*?
   - a. Turn the fine adjustment knob.
   - b. Put a drop of water on the slide.
   - c. Place the slide on the microscope stage.
   - d. Clean the microscope slide.
4. What type of information is given in the Conclusions section?
   - a. instruments needed for the investigation
   - b. questions to be answered by doing the investigation
   - c. additional information about the investigation
   - d. steps to follow when carrying out the investigation

Use the lines below to write your answers for numbers 5 and 6. Your PLAN graphic can help you.

5. Why do you think lab observations are organized in step-by-step order?

____

____

____

____

Test Tip

Question 6 asks you to make a prediction. Think about what you've learned about conducting an experiment. Then think about what might happen if you did the steps in a different order.

6. Predict some problems that might occur if a student conducted the procedure steps out of order.

____

____

____

____

Unit 4 Review

Reading in Science

In this unit, you have practiced using the KWL Plus, Outlining, PACA, and PLAN reading strategies. Choose one strategy and use it when you read the selection below. Use a separate sheet of paper to draw charts, take notes, and summarize what you learn.

Hint *Remember that all reading strategies have activities for before, during, and after reading. To review these steps, look back at Unit 1 or at the last page of this book.*

Twilight Zone of the Ocean

We are going deep. Down here, between 450 feet and 3,300 feet (137 and 1,005 meters) below the surface of the sea, it is dark. The pressure is from 15 to 100 times greater than it is on land. Unless humans are in special submarines, they are crushed to death by the weight of the water.

Yet, there is life down here. There is little to eat. No plants can grow—there is not enough sunlight to make food. Most of the creatures here are both hunters and hunted. If you were to travel this deep, here are some of the creatures you might see.

The Squid, *Heterotheuthis*

This tiny squid, perhaps four inches long, has a huge eye. It also has a secret weapon. When attacked, this squid shoots glowing ink. That ink will confuse an attacker.

Heterotheuthis is always looking for its own meal, though. When it sees a tiny shrimp scoot past, it springs into action. It forces water from its body and moves to catch the shrimp.

The Ocean Earthworm, *Tomopteris*

These worms of the ocean are about four inches long. They don't look like earthworms. Each has what looks like tiny paddles along its body. As it swims, the *Tomopteris* moves like a snake sliding sideways over the sand. You can see through its body.

The Jellyfish, *Benthocodon hyalinus*

First discovered in 1987, these rare jellyfish have only been seen about a dozen times. They look like alien spaceships.

Benthocodon looks like a clear blob, but inside the blob is a red blotch. That is the jellyfish's stomach. The animals who live this deep cannot see the red. The light rays from above absorb that color. Some scientists think that the stomach is red to hide any glowing animals the jellyfish eats.

The Bat of the Sea, *Bathocyroe fosteri*

This odd-looking, transparent animal looks like a bat, but it is known as a comb jelly. The *Bathocyroe* and the other comb jellies do not have stingers like jellyfish. They are called comb jellies because they have eight comb-plates. These plates are groups of hairlike fibers that help the comb jelly move through the water. When it is alarmed, the *Bathocyroe* flaps its winglike parts. That helps it move through the water even more quickly.

Phronima sedentaria

She is a clever mother, *Phronima sedentaria.* As she gets ready to lay her eggs, this crustacean seeks out a salp. Salps are sea animals that have barrel-shaped bodies. *Phronima* catches and kills a salp. Then she eats out the salp's insides, leaving the barrel. In this way, she turns the salp's body into a firm house for her eggs.

When she is ready to lay her eggs, *Phronima* grabs the sides of the hollowed-out barrel with her claws. Until the eggs hatch, the salp's body is her home.

Down here in the deep ocean, the ways animals live seem strange to those of us who live on land. But each of the animals has found a way to survive in this odd, sunless world.

Use your notes and charts to help you answer the questions below.

1. Humans cannot easily survive deep underwater because
   a. they would be crushed by the pressure.
   b. they cannot defend themselves against the animals there.
   c. oxygen tanks do not work deep underwater.
   d. the water is too cold.
2. What does the squid *Heterotheuthis* do when it is attacked?
   a. It changes color to confuse an attacker.
   b. It fights with the animal that is attacking it.
   c. It shoots glowing ink to confuse an attacker.
   d. It runs and hides in a deep cave.
3. *Phronima sedentaria* uses a salp's body to lay its eggs in because
   a. the salp's body also provides food for the young.
   b. *Phronima* needs a place to rest.
   c. the salp is a male *Phronima.*
   d. the salp's body protects the eggs.
4. Describe the ways animals protect themselves deep underwater.

____

____

Unit 5
Reading in Mathematics

When you read the statistics in the sports section of the newspaper, you are reading mathematics. When you read a recipe, you are reading mathematics. When you figure out how much it will cost you to buy a car, you are reading mathematics. As you can see, mathematics reading goes far beyond your textbooks.

How Mathematics Reading Is Organized

Reading mathematics is different from other kinds of reading. When you read mathematics, you must pay attention to symbols, numbers, and equations. You must also make sure you understand one topic before you go on to the next. Much of mathematics builds on what you already know. If you don't learn one topic, you will find the next topic very difficult. Recognizing patterns in mathematics reading will help you understand what you read. Here are some common patterns you may see.

Diagrams and Graphs. In mathematics, sometimes a diagram or graph represents the main point of the reading. The text before and after the diagram or graph explains it. When you see this pattern, you know that you must pay attention to the graph or diagram. You can better understand what the text is saying if you redraw the diagram yourself and write an explanation of the concept.

Obtuse Angles

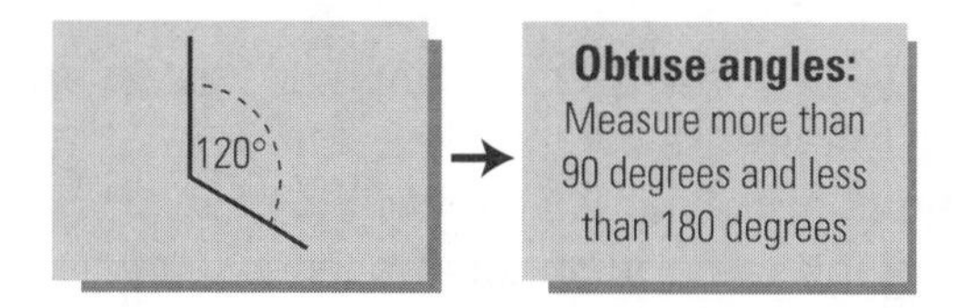

Formulas and Equations. Often, a mathematics lesson will be based on equations and formulas. Carefully look at each symbol. Once you know each symbol's meaning, you can move on. When you see equations and formulas, it is also a clue that you need to be able to use the formula before you move on. Prove to yourself you understand it by working problems based on either the formula or the equation.

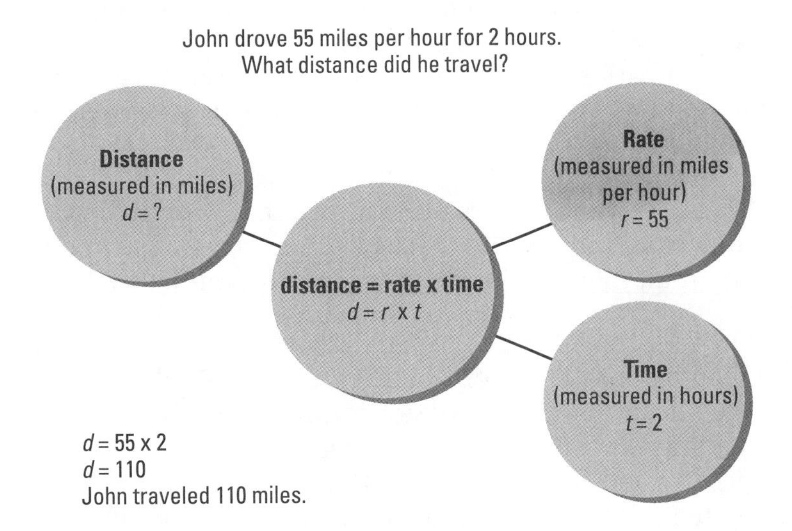

Steps of a Process. Much of mathematics reading describes a process. For example, you might read the instructions from your bank on balancing your checking account. In a textbook, you might read the steps of the process for multiplying decimals. When you see this pattern, you know to look for the next step as you read. Here are two tips to getting the most out of this pattern. First, rewrite the steps in your own words, so you know you understand them. Second, try several examples to make sure you understand the process.

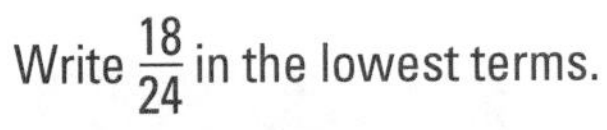

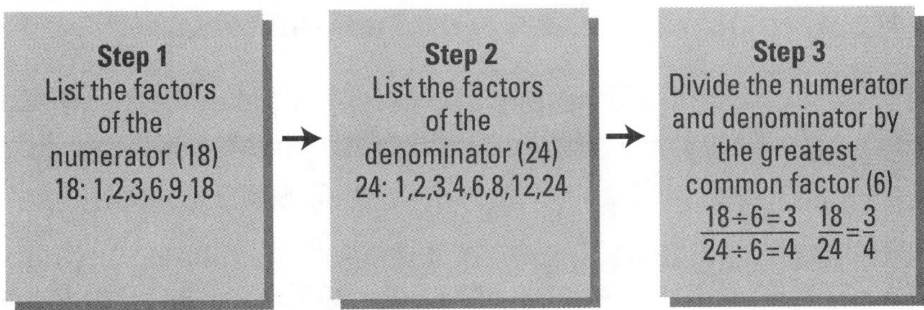

Getting the Most from Your Reading

If you can recognize the way a reading is organized, you will be better able to understand what you read. You will be able to think about what kind of information might be next and how all the points in the reading fit together. Drawing word maps like the ones on these two pages can show you these patterns. Thinking about how a reading is organized can help you understand—and remember—what you read.

Lesson 19 Number Sense: Number Patterns

Understand It...... Most people have a morning routine. They follow the same pattern every morning. A pattern is anything that occurs in a repeated order, or sequence. There are many different kinds of patterns. Floor tiles often have a pattern. House numbers on a street have a pattern. The route a school bus takes has a pattern. Even your school day has a pattern.

Hint

You can review the PACA strategy on page 12.

Try It............... This selection explores number patterns. Use the PACA strategy to help you understand the reading. Start by predicting what you will learn. Think about all the kinds of number patterns you know.

On a separate piece of paper, draw your own PACA chart like the one below. Record your predictions in the Predictions column of the chart. Then read the selection. After you read, confirm or revise your predictions. If your reading confirms a prediction, write a check mark in the left column. If you need to add or revise a prediction, write a star in the left column. Finally, write information that supports all of these points in the Support column.

Strategy Tip

Look at the title and subheadings of the selection as you preview it. What do you think you will learn? Record your predictions in your PACA chart.

Predictions	Support

Vocabulary Tip

Do you know what a sequence is? Look at the sentences that follow the word. The sentence gives the meaning of the term.

Number Patterns

Leonardo Fibonacci was a great European mathematician. In the 12th century, he identified this number sequence:

1, 1, 2, 3, 5, 8, 13, ...

The Fibonacci sequence is a number pattern. The terms that make up the pattern have a relationship. In this relationship the pattern does not change. It goes on and on.

Look at the first two terms of the Fibonacci sequence. They are 1 and 1. Look at the third term. How are 1 and 1 related to 2? Look at the second and third terms. How are 1 and 2 related to 3? Look at the third and fourth terms. How are 2 and 3 related to 5? Each term is the sum of the two terms that come before it. This pattern does not change. It is constant.

The square of a series of whole numbers has a different kind of pattern. Look at the chart on the next page. Study each line. Look for a constant relationship.

$1^2 = 1$

$2^2 = 4 = 1 + 3$

$3^2 = 9 = 1 + 3 + 5$

$4^2 = 16 = 1 + 3 + 5 + 7$

$5^2 = 25 = 1 + 3 + 5 + 7 + 9$

Do you see the pattern? The value of 1^2 is the first odd number, or 1. The value of 2^2 is the sum of the first two odd numbers, or 4. The value of 3^2 is the sum of the first three odd numbers, or 9. You can use that addition pattern to find the square of any whole number. The value of 7^2 is the sum of the first seven odd numbers. What is that value?

Number Patterns in Daily Life

Many businesses use number patterns to predict their future sales. They record yearly sales information. They review the information and identify patterns. Then they make predictions based on these patterns.

Maggie's Framing Company sells picture frames. The company has been in business for three years. During the first year, the company sold 3,208 picture frames. In the second year, the company sold 3,528 frames. During the third year, 4,056 frames were sold.

Vocabulary Tip

Notice that the word *data* is in bold type. Sometimes, writers define words by using examples. Here, the writer defines *data* by giving you examples in the three sentences before the word is used.

The company owner analyzed that **data**. She discovered that between the first and second years, sales increased by 10 percent. Between the second and third years, the company's sales increased by 15 percent. The owner used that trend to make predictions about sales for the next two years. She predicted that sales would increase by 20 percent in the fourth year and by 25 percent in the fifth year. The predictions helped her plan for the future. She hired more workers to make the frames. She also hired more salesclerks. Now she will be able to keep up with increased demand for her unusual frames.

Number patterns can help determine how many firefighters a city needs.

Number patterns help communities plan for the future, too. Town officials gather information about their community's population. They look for patterns in the data. Sometimes the number patterns show a steady increase in population. That means more people will need town services. Officials must make plans for future growth. They might need to hire more firefighters or build more schools. Sometimes the number patterns show a steady decrease in population. Fewer people will need town services. Officials make plans to reduce the number of town employees or even to close schools.

Number patterns have probably led to predictions about your community. The next time you see a new traffic light, street sign, or improved road, think of a number pattern!

Now look back at the predictions you made. Revise the ones that were incorrect. Add information you didn't predict. Write stars next to any predictions that you added or revised. Then be sure to add information that supports your predictions.

Apply It........... To check your understanding of the selection, circle the best answer to each of the following questions.

1. All number patterns involve
   - **a.** a sum.
   - **b.** multiplication.
   - **c.** a relationship.
   - **d.** a steady decrease.
2. The tone of this selection is
   - **a.** humorous.
   - **b.** sad.
   - **c.** mysterious.
   - **d.** informative.
3. Suppose your town government notices that the population of the town is falling. What might happen after officials see this number pattern?
   - **a.** Voters might elect a new mayor.
   - **b.** The number of firefighters might be reduced.
   - **c.** An old school might be repainted.
   - **d.** Your class might go on a field trip.
4. What is data?
   - **a.** a prediction
   - **b.** a collection of information
   - **c.** the manager of a company
   - **d.** a future occurrence

Test Tip

To correctly answer question 3, you must identify a cause-and-effect relationship. The question states the cause: Officials see a new number pattern. The correct answer identifies what happens —the effect— as a result of the cause.

5. The sequence 1, 19, 5, 2, 33, … is *not* a number pattern because the terms
   a. do not show a constant relationship.
   b. are steadily increasing.
   c. increase and then decrease.
   d. change in the same manner.

Use the lines below to write your answers for numbers 6 and 7. You can use your PACA notes to help you.

6. Look at the following number pattern: 11, 13, 17, 25, …. Explain how to identify the next three terms in the pattern.

____

____

____

____

7. Suppose that number patterns show that the population of your community will increase by 1,000 people each year for the next ten years. What should be done to prepare for that growth? Write a letter to town officials describing three things that must be changed.

____

____

____

____

Lesson 20 Numerical Operations: Russian Peasant Multiplication Method

Understand It...... Can you find the product of two factors without multiplying? You can if you know the Russian Peasant Multiplication Method. In this selection, you will learn this multiplication process. Use the KWL Plus strategy to help you understand the steps.

Hint
You can review the KWL Plus strategy on page 4.

Try It.............. Begin by drawing a KWL chart like the one below on a separate sheet of paper. Then list everything you know about multiplication in the K column. In the W column, write what you want to know about the Russian Peasant Multiplication Method. After you read, write the answers to your questions in the L column.

K (What I know)	W (What I want to know)	L (What I've learned)

Strategy Tip
The reading describes a series of steps. Clue words tell you the order in which the steps should be completed. Words such as *then*, *next*, and *finally* show sequence.

Vocabulary Tip
The word *omits* means "leaves out." If you omit a decimal, you leave it out.

Russian Peasant Multiplication Method

Yesterday, 26 boxes of compact discs were delivered to Al's Music Shop. Each box holds 35 CDs. Al needs to label each disc. The store manager, Beth, wants to know how many labels she needs. She does this by finding the product of 26 and 35. However, Beth does not multiply to find the answer. Instead, she makes two columns. Beth marks one column *Halve* and the other column *Double*. Then she puts the first factor in the first column and the second factor in the second column.

Halve	Double
26	35

Next, Beth finds one-half of 26. She writes 13 in the first column. She doubles 35 and writes 70 in the second column.

Halve	Double
26	35
13	70

Beth continues finding half of each amount in the first column. (If one-half of a number is a whole number and a decimal, she **omits** the decimal.) In the second column, Beth continues doubling numbers. She repeats this process until the last entry in the first column is 1. Finally, her columns look like this:

Halve	Double
26	35
13	70
6	140
3	280
1	560

Now, Beth circles all the even numbers in the first column. She circles 26 and 6. She crosses out the numbers directly across from the circled numbers, or 35 and 140. Finally, Beth adds the remaining numbers in the second column. She finds that the sum of 70 + 280 + 560 is 910. Beth goes to the storeroom to get 910 labels.

Halve	Double
(26)	~~35~~
13	70
(6)	~~140~~
3	280
1	560
	910

Strategy Tip

As you preview the selection, notice the two subheadings: "How Many Ice Cream Cones Are Needed?" and "Which Method Do You Prefer?" What do you think these sections will be about?

How Many Ice Cream Cones Are Needed?

During the month of July, Sweet Treat Ice Cream store used 52 boxes of ice cream cones. Each box contained 48 cones. You can use the Russian Peasant Multiplication Method to find the total number of cones used during July. Begin by making two columns. Label the first column *Halve* and the second column *Double*. Write 52 in the first column. Write 48 in the second column.

Do you remember what to do next? Find one-half of 52, or 26. Write 26 in the first column. Across from it, write 96, which is 48 doubled. Continue until the last entry in the first column is 1. (Remember, if half of a number is a whole number and decimal, omit the decimal.)

Now, circle all the even numbers in the first column. Cross out the numbers directly across from them in the second column. Add the remaining doubles. You should find that the Sweet Treat Ice Cream store used 2,496 cones during July.

Which Method Do You Prefer?

You probably learned to multiply to find a product. In the Russian Peasant Multiplication Method, you halve, double, and add to find a product. Although the method may be new to you, it will give you what you are looking for—the correct answer! So the next time you need to find the product of two factors, try this new method instead of multiplying.

Now that you have finished reading the selection, complete the L column of your KWL chart with information you have learned. Instead of writing a summary of the selection, create a problem and solve it. That will prove that you understand the Russian Peasant Multiplication Method.

Numerical Operations: Russian Peasant Multiplication Method

Apply It. . . . . To check your understanding of the selection, circle the best answer to each of the following questions.

1. The author wrote this selection to
   a. explain how addition and multiplication are related.
   b. explore customs from other cultures.
   c. analyze life in Russia.
   d. describe the steps in a mathematical process.

2. When you use the Russian Peasant Multiplication Method, what should you do first?
   a. Set up a multiplication problem.
   b. Make two columns.
   c. Add the factors.
   d. Find the difference of the factors.

3. Why did Beth get 910 labels from the storeroom?
   a. There were 910 CDs.
   b. She expected 910 customers that month.
   c. A delivery of 910 boxes had just arrived.
   d. She had to fill 910 orders.

Test Tip
Reviewing the examples and the charts in the selection can help you find the answer to question 4.

4. What is the next step after circling all the even numbers in the first column?
   a. Find the product of the remaining numbers.
   b. Circle the odd numbers in the second column.
   c. Cross out the numbers directly across from them.
   d. Find the sum of all the numbers in the second column.

Use the lines below to write your answers for numbers 5 and 6. Use your KWL chart to help you.

5. Write a letter to a friend that explains the Russian Peasant Multiplication Method. Make up a problem and draw a chart to explain the process.

____

____

____

Test Tip
The L column of your KWL chart can help you answer question 6.

6. Suppose you need to find the product of two numbers. Which process would you use? Explain your choice.

____

____

____

Lesson 21 Number Sense: Understanding Remainders

Understand It...... Years ago you learned how to divide. You discovered that some numbers do not go evenly into other numbers. You saw that some final answers have a remainder. In this selection, you will learn more about remainders. You will recognize relationships between remainders and the final answer.

Hint
You can review the PLAN strategy on page 16.

Try It.............. The PLAN strategy can help you "see" these relationships. The first step in this strategy is to predict what you will read in the article. Preview the selection for clues about how the information is organized. Does it seem to center on one topic? Are two things compared? Is information given in time order? Once you have decided on the way the ideas are organized, you can choose a word map to help you understand it.

Your next step is to copy one of the word maps below or to create one of your own on another sheet of paper. Predict what the main points of the article will be. Then read the article. As you read a second time, locate important information. Write check marks next to ideas you know something about. Write question marks next to information you don't know about. Then add words to your map that will help you remember that information. Later, you will note what you have learned.

Strategy Tip
Before you make a prediction, think about what you know about remainders. When do you see remainders in math class? When do you see remainders in your everyday life?

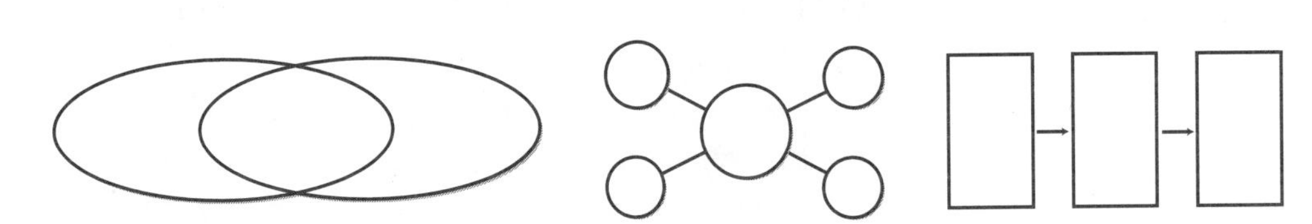

Vocabulary Tip
In math, the *dividend* is the number is being divided. The *divisor* is the number by which the dividend is being divided. What word do you see *inside* both of these words?

Understanding Remainders

A remainder is something that is left over. In math, the answer to a division problem can have a remainder. That occurs when a **divisor** does not go into a **dividend** evenly. Something remains, or is left over.

In your everyday life, you will solve many division problems. Often, these problems will have a remainder. In many real-life situations, the remainder must be interpreted. Sometimes, a remainder will mean that you will add 1 to the final answer. At other times, the remainder can be ignored. How will you know what to do? You will learn to look at the problem situation to see what to do about the remainder.

The Craft Fair
Millville High is having a craft fair. Kyle wants to sell birdhouses at the fair. He uses 2 meters of wire in every birdhouse he makes. The week before the fair, Kyle discovers he has 9 meters of wire. He wants to

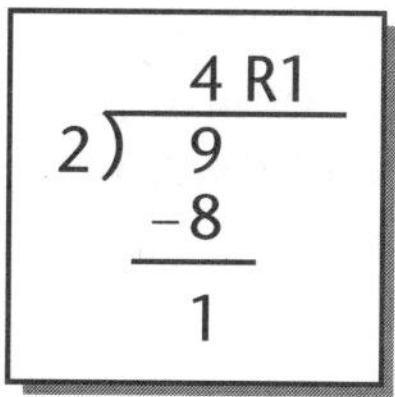

find out how many birdhouses he can make. Kyle divides 9 by 2. His answer is 4 Remainder 1. Kyle thinks about the remainder. How many birdhouses can he make? The remainder represents part of a birdhouse. He realizes that he should ignore the remainder. Kyle discovers that he can make four birdhouses.

Sue also wants to sell crafts at the fair. She decides to make 20 photograph albums. Sue already has most of the materials she needs. She needs only 8 inches of lace for each album. Sue multiplies 20 by 8 to figure out how much lace to buy. She needs 160 inches of lace.

13 R4
12)160
12
40
36
4

Sue then visits a local craft shop. The shop sells lace only by the foot. Sue divides 160 by 12. Her answer is 13 Remainder 4. Sue knows the shop will not sell less than a foot of lace. So she adds 1 to the 13. She purchases 14 feet of lace. Now she has enough lace for all 20 albums.

The two craft makers faced similar situations. The answers to their division problems had remainders. Both crafters had to decide what to do with the remainder. They thought about the relationship between the remainder and the situation in the problem. Kyle realized that he should ignore the remainder. Sue realized that she needed to add 1 to her final answer. Different situations call for different actions.

The Competition

Three bands from Millville are going to a competition. The band directors need to order buses for the event. A total of 405 band members will attend. Each bus can hold 48 people. So one director divides 405 by 48. Her quotient is 8 Remainder 21. What should she do with the remainder? Should she ignore it? Or should she add 1 to 8?

Think about the relationship between the remainder and the problem situation. The dividend is the total number of band members attending the competition. The divisor is the number of members who can ride on each bus. So the whole number in the quotient shows how many buses are full. The remainder shows how many band members are left over. However, these people still need a ride. Therefore, the group needs nine buses to travel to the competition. Eight of the buses will be full. The ninth bus will carry only 21 members.

Suppose the director had ignored the remainder. Twenty-one band members would have been left on the sidewalk! Luckily for them, the director understood remainders.

Now that you have finished reading the selection, think about what you have read. Then note what you have learned in your word map. You might note how you use remainders in your everyday life. You might also note the definitions of the math terms *dividend* and *divisor*.

Apply It............ To check your understanding of the selection, circle the best answer to each question below.

1. The main idea of this selection is that
   a. every remainder can be ignored.
   b. whenever you have a remainder, you should add 1 to the final answer.
   c. a remainder must be interpreted.
   d. a remainder means you made a mistake.

2. What does the word *remainder* mean in this selection?
   a. an odd number
   b. a number you can divide evenly
   c. something that you can ignore
   d. something that is left over

Test Tip

Question 3 asks you about opinions. An *opinion* is a person's thoughts or feelings about a subject. The correct answer is a statement that cannot be proven true.

3. Which of the following statements is an opinion?
   a. Band competitions are enjoyable events.
   b. Sue bought 14 feet of lace.
   c. Some crafters keep a supply of materials available.
   d. The group needs nine buses to travel to the competition.

4. What would have happened if Sue had ignored her remainder?
   a. She would only have been able to make 19 albums.
   b. She would have been able to make all 20 albums.
   c. She would have made too many albums.
   d. She would have made too few albums.

5. The band director orders nine buses. That means she
   a. has not ordered enough buses.
   b. knows that having a remainder can mean adding 1 to a final answer.
   c. knows that remainders are not important in ordering buses.
   d. has ordered too many buses.

Use the lines below to write your answers for numbers 6 and 7. Use your PLAN graphic to help you.

6. Describe two real-life situations when a remainder could be ignored.

____

____

____

7. Describe a real-life situation in which a person should add 1 to a final answer.

____

____

____

Lesson 22 Economics: The Billion Dollar Party

Understand It...... Have you ever watched the Olympic Games? If so, you saw thousands of people come together for sports events. In this selection, you will learn about what goes on before the games begin. You will discover what the host country must do to prepare for the games. Since you probably know about the Olympic Games, KWL may be a good reading strategy to use.

Hint

You can review the KWL Plus strategy on page 4.

Try It.............. To begin using the KWL Plus strategy, copy the chart below onto a separate sheet of paper. List what you know about the Olympic Games in the K column. In the W column, write what you want to know about hosting the Games. Think about these questions as you read the selection. After you read, write what you have learned in the L column.

Strategy Tip

You may know a great deal about the topic of a selection. If you do, previewing will help you narrow the list of things you will write in the K column. It can also help you ask questions in the W column that the selection will answer.

K (What I know)	W (What I want to know)	L (What I've learned)

The Billion Dollar Party

Have you or your parents ever hosted a large party? How many people attended? Ten? Twenty? Whatever the number of guests, you probably discovered that large parties are expensive. Now suppose you had to host a celebration for 10,000 people. A party that big might sound impossible to organize, but it's not. It happens every four years in the summer and every four years in the winter. Let the Games begin!

The first modern Olympic Games were held in 1896 in Athens, Greece. Fourteen nations sent a total of 245 athletes to the event. One hundred years later, more than 10,000 athletes competed in the games held in Atlanta, Georgia. An equal number of trainers and coaches also attended. When journalists and **spectators** were added, the number swelled into the millions.

Vocabulary Tip

Sometimes you can figure out a word's meaning by thinking about words that are similar to it. *Spectators* is similar to *spectacles*, another word for *glasses*. Glasses help you *see*; spectators come to *see* an event.

No matter who hosts the Olympics, everyone who attends needs a place to stay. They also need meals and transportation to the events.

Then there is the problem of staging the Games. Stadiums and practice areas must be built. Athletes in many events need special equipment. Summer games require huge pools for swimming and diving events. Winter athletes need snowy slopes for alpine skiing.

All these details must be taken care of long before the Games begin. They require money—lots of money.

The finish line!

Vocabulary Tip

You can figure out the meaning of *prestige* by thinking about the sentences around it. Why would a city want to host the Olympics? Think about the reasons the writer gives in this paragraph.

A look at the price tag for the 1996 games shows just how expensive hosting the Olympics can be. Before the start of the Games, organizers spent more than $500 million to prepare. Preparations included figuring out how much it would cost Atlanta to host the Games, doing publicity, and planning for everyone's needs. It also included creating new roads, event sites, and buildings. Atlanta spent another $1 billion during the Games. This money was used for such things as security and the actual competitions.

Who pays these huge bills? Most of the cost of the Atlanta Games was covered by private funding. Television networks paid large sums for the right to broadcast the Olympics to more than 2.5 billion people worldwide. The sale of tickets for events earned hundreds of thousands of dollars. Large companies, or corporate sponsors, donated money.

Benefits or Boos?

The costs are staggering. The planning takes years. People are quick to point out mistakes. Why would any city want to host the Olympics?

Prestige is one answer. The Olympic Games are a worldwide event. They offer the host city and country an opportunity to show off in front of billions of people. The Games are a worldwide travel advertisement.

The Olympic Games also add to the local economy. Thousands of jobs are created. The companies that build stadiums and housing need workers. The buildings remain after the athletes leave town. Local residents find ways to use them.

Perhaps the main reason for hosting the Games is less obvious. The city or country may want to be part of a tradition, a tradition that has lasted for hundreds of years. The Olympic Games celebrate sports, the athletes, and personal success. They also symbolize the unity of nations.

Now that you have finished reading the selection, fill in the L column of your chart. Be sure you answer the questions you wrote in the W column. If the article doesn't answer your questions, you probably can find this information in newspaper or magazine articles. If you find information about questions you didn't ask, add these facts to your L column. When you finish your KWL chart, write a summary of what you have learned about hosting the Olympic Games.

Apply It............ To check your understanding of the selection, circle the best answer to each of the following questions.

1. What is the main idea of the selection?
   a. Public funds should cover the cost of hosting the Olympic Games.
   b. There are many benefits to hosting the Olympics.
   c. Only countries with large populations should host the Olympic Games.
   d. Preparing for the Olympics is a long and costly process.

2. How much money did Atlanta, Georgia, spend preparing for the 1996 Olympic Games?
   a. $500 million
   b. $1 billion
   c. $5 million
   d. $500 billion

Test Tip

Question 3 asks which choice is *not* a benefit of hosting the Olympics. Think about each choice. Ask if it *is* or *is not* a benefit before you choose an answer.

3. Which of the following is *not* a benefit of hosting the Olympic Games?
   a. The local economy gets a boost.
   b. People all over the world learn about the host city.
   c. New buildings are constructed.
   d. Local athletes have a better chance of winning their events.
4. What is corporate sponsorship?
   a. jobs offered to Olympic athletes
   b. money donated to the Olympics by large companies
   c. a way to decide which city or country will host the Olympics
   d. both a and b

Test Tip

The word *reason* in question 5 is a clue to look for a cause-and-effect relationship. The question states the *effect*. Which answer would *cause* the Olympics to be so expensive?

5. What is one reason the Olympic Games are so expensive for the host city?
   a. The number of events has stayed the same over time.
   b. The number of medals awarded has decreased in the past few years.
   c. The number of spectators has continually declined.
   d. The number of countries sending athletes to the Olympics has increased.

Use the lines below to write your answers for numbers 6 and 7. Use your KWL chart to help you.

6. Pretend you are a member of an Olympics planning committee. Make a list of at least five jobs your committee must do before the Games begin.

___

___

___

___

___

7. Do you think your community would benefit from hosting the Olympics? Express your views in a letter to the editor of a local newspaper.

___

___

___

___

___

Lesson 23 Math History: Florence Nightingale, Crusading Nurse

Understand It...... This article is about Florence Nightingale. She was a pioneer in the field of nursing. More than 100 years ago, Nightingale created medical procedures that are used in hospitals today. Florence Nightingale also contributed greatly to the field of mathematics. In this article, you will discover her little-known contribution.

Hint
You can review the outlining strategy on page 8.

Try It.............. Making an outline will help you understand this article. Look at the title and the subheadings. You might write each subheading on a separate Roman-numeral line of your outline. List supporting details on the capital-letter and number lines underneath each one. Fill in your outline after you read.

I. ______
  A. ______
  B. ______
    1. ______
    2. ______
II. ______
  A. ______
  B. ______
    1. ______
    2. ______

Strategy Tip
Look at the title and the subheadings. What do they tell you about the way the article is organized? Do you see any dates? If so, you can tell if the article is organized in time order. Also preview the first and last paragraph to look for clues to the way the article is organized.

Florence Nightingale, Crusading Nurse

Have you ever visited a hospital? If so, you probably remember a very clean building. Hospital staffs work hard to keep germs from spreading. They know that cleanliness is the key to stopping the spread of infection.

That was not always the case. The hospitals of long ago were quite different. Patients' rooms had little fresh air. Supplies were few. Dirt was everywhere. It may seem odd, but scientists have only known for about 100 years that dirt and germs carry disease.

That all changed because of the hard work of a woman named Florence Nightingale. She dedicated her life to reforming medical care.

Early Life

Florence Nightingale was born on May 12, 1820, in Florence, Italy. Her parents named her after the city where she was born. Her father was a wealthy Englishman. Her mother was a strong-willed woman. She wanted Florence and her sister to live a life of social **prominence**. She wanted them to be friendly with well-known people and to go to fashionable parties. Social events were the focus of their lives.

Vocabulary Tip
Do you know what *prominence* means? Look at the sentences that follow it for clues.

Math History:
Florence Nightingale, Crusading Nurse

The family moved to England when Florence was a young girl. Her mother taught her and her sister about society and running a home. Mr. Nightingale taught his daughters history and philosophy. At that time, girls rarely studied these subjects.

As a teenager, Florence was surrounded by friends and relatives. The family traveled often. However, Florence wanted a fuller life. She was not content with marrying well and raising a family. She wanted to serve others, but she wasn't sure how to start.

At the age of 22, Nightingale discovered her lifework. She learned of the Institute of Protestant Deaconesses in Kaiserswerth, Germany, that trained nurses in hospital work. Nightingale began studying health. She read all she could about caring for the sick. For two years, she hid her interest from her family. Finally, she found the courage to tell her parents. Nightingale told them she wanted to attend the institute to become a nurse. Mrs. Nightingale refused to allow her daughter to enroll.

Strategy Tip

Have you written "A Life of Nursing" on a Roman-numeral line in your outline? If so, add the details in this section about Nightingale's nursing career on the capital-letter and number lines.

A Life of Nursing

Six years later, Florence Nightingale finally got her wish. Against the will of her parents, she entered the Institute. After completing her studies, she returned to London and became director of a women's hospital. Nightingale set about changing the hospital. She made sure the patients received nutritious food. She made sure the patients' rooms had fresh air. Most important, she taught the staff how to keep the hospital clean.

Soon after Nightingale arrived at the hospital, England and France declared war on Russia. English soldiers were hurt or killed in large numbers. Nightingale wanted to do something for her countrymen. She left for the battlefield with a handful of nurses.

Nightingale was shocked at what she found. Wounded soldiers filled a filthy hospital that was short on food, supplies, and staff. Nightingale went to work. With the help of others, she scrubbed the place. She trained nurses. She made sure the patients received healthful meals. Her efforts paid off.

Within a year, the death rate fell more than 20 percent. The grateful patients nicknamed Nightingale "The lady with the lamp." She brought light and air and hope to a hospital that had been just another place to die.

Contribution to Mathematics

News of Nightingale's achievements spread. When she returned to England, she met with Queen Victoria. The British War Department asked for her advice on how to help the wounded. Nightingale wrote an 800-page report detailing her work. While preparing this report,

Vocabulary Tip

In the term *pie chart,* think of what a pie looks like. What is its shape and how is it cut? Drawing a mental picture can help you understand a term.

Nightingale created the "polar-area diagram." It presented a picture of her data. Today, we know the "polar-area diagram" as a **pie chart**. It is a popular method of picturing information. Pie charts show how all of the pieces of information on a subject relate to one another.

After she sent in her report, Nightingale's health began to decline. She spent much of her time in bed. However, she still wrote about caring for the sick. She also continued to suggest hospital reforms. In 1910, Nightingale died.

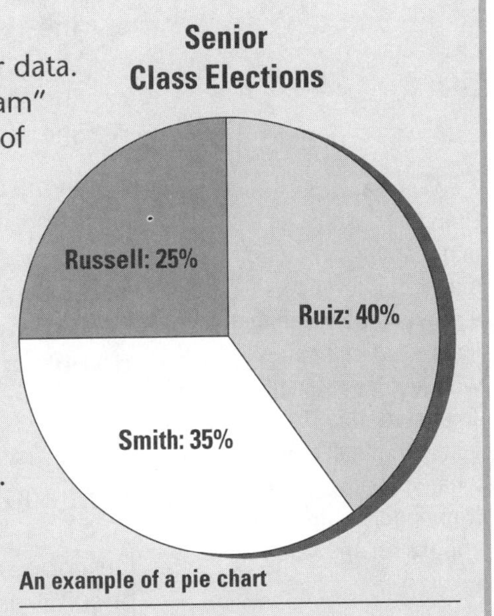

An example of a pie chart

Now that you have finished reading the article, write your outline. Then review it. Does it give you a quick overview of the main points of the article? If not, add or revise it as needed. Then use your outline to help you write a summary of the article.

Apply It........... To check your understanding of the article, circle the best answer to each question below.

1. What did Mrs. Nightingale want her daughters to become?
   a. nurses
   b. doctors
   c. wives and mothers
   d. teachers
2. How did Florence Nightingale become interested in nursing?
   a. She heard about an institute in Germany.
   b. She visited a hospital in Italy.
   c. Her mother was once a nurse.
   d. Her father was a doctor.
3. What did Nightingale do after she became interested in nursing?
   a. She went to college.
   b. She read about caring for the sick.
   c. She did volunteer work in a hospital.
   d. She asked her parents if she could attend nursing school.

Math History: Florence Nightingale, Crusading Nurse

4. What did Nightingale contribute to mathematics?
   a. She invented the bar graph.
   b. She taught other women how to solve math problems.
   c. She showed patients how to perform calculations.
   d. She invented the pie chart.

Test Tip

Question 5 asks you to make an *inference*. To make an inference, you "read between the lines," or think about what you've learned. To answer this question, think about what you know about Nightingale before you choose an answer.

5. Why was the drop in the death rate in the hospital important to Nightingale?
   a. She would become depressed if a patient died.
   b. She needed a reason to ask for additional nurses.
   c. It showed that her methods worked.
   d. both a and b

Use the lines below to write your answers for numbers 6 and 7. You can use your outline to help you.

6. Describe some of the ways that Florence Nightingale changed the care of hospital patients.

____

____

____

7. Write a letter to the editor that suggests making a stamp to honor Florence Nightingale's life and work. Include a sketch of a possible design.

____

____

____

Lesson 24 Problem Solving: Finding Relevant Information

Understand It...... Anyone who has ever taken a math class has solved word problems. A word problem describes a situation. It asks a question about the situation. To answer the question, the reader must perform some type of calculation. In this selection you will learn how to read—and solve—word problems.

Hint
You can review the PACA strategy on page 12.

Try It.............. Since you probably know something about word problems, PACA is a good reading strategy to use. Draw a PACA chart like the one below on a separate sheet of paper. First, preview the selection and predict what you will learn. Record your predictions in the Predictions column of your chart. Then read the selection. After reading, confirm or revise your predictions. Add a check mark next to predictions you confirm. Write stars next to predictions you add or revise. Finally, write details that support your predictions in the Support column.

Strategy Tip
Think about how you have solved word problems in math. What did you do first? next? Use these ideas to make predictions on what this selection will be about.

Predictions	Support

Vocabulary Tip
Do you know what *relevant* means? Look at the words that follow the term. They contain a synonym for *relevant*. What is the synonym?

Finding Relevant Information

Every word problem asks a question. Every word problem contains information. The reader must use the information in the problem to answer that question. Some of the information is **relevant**, or related, to the problem. Some of the information is not relevant—that is, it is unnecessary. A good problem solver focuses on relevant information. A good problem solver has a plan for finding the correct answer.

Create a Plan

- The first step in the plan is to read the problem carefully. Determine what you are being asked to find out. This is the question you must answer.
- Then make a list of all the information contained in the problem. Include everything.

Do these students have a plan?

Strategy Tip

This selection has two kinds of lists: bulleted lists, or lists with dots, and numbered lists. Lists often show important information. Pay attention to them when you preview a selection.

- Next, look over your list. Think about what you are being asked to find out. Cross out any information in your list that is not relevant to the question. Circle the information that will help you answer the question.
- Finally, use the relevant information to solve the problem. Complete the steps to find the answer.

Use this plan to solve the following word problem:

The Sweater Shop has been in business for 27 years. The shop has been so busy that the owners had to hire three more workers. If business continues to be this good, the owners might open another store. December was the busiest month in the history of the shop. Sales for the month totaled $34,528. If this was $9,017 more than the sales for the previous month, what was November's sales total?

Put Your Plan to Work

Now think about what the problem asks you to find out. The last sentence of the problem contains this question. You must determine the sales total for November.

Next, make a list of all the information contained in the problem. Your list should look like this:

1. The shop has been in business for 27 years.
2. The owners hired three new workers.
3. The owners are thinking about opening another store.
4. December was the busiest month in the history of the shop.
5. December sales totaled $34,528.
6. December's sales total was $9,017 more than the sales for the previous month.

Review the list. Think about the question. What information will not help you find November's sales total? Items 1, 2, 3, and 4 are not relevant. Cross them out. Look at items 5 and 6. They will help you find November's sales total. Circle these items.

Use the circled items to solve the word problem. Because December's total was *more* than November's total, you need to set up a subtraction problem. You will subtract $9,017 from $34,528. The answer is $25,511. This means that the sales total for November was $25,511.

You can use this plan to solve any kind of word problem. It will help you collect and organize information. It will also help you focus on what information is relevant to the problem.

Now that you have finished reading the selection, revise or change any predictions that were incorrect. Mark these predictions with a star. Then add details that support your predictions in the Support column.

Apply It. . . . . To check your understanding of the selection, circle the best answer to each question below.

1. What is the first thing to do after reading a problem?
   - **a.** Set up a math problem.
   - **b.** Decide what you are being asked to find out.
   - **c.** Perform the calculations.
   - **d.** Make a list of all the information contained in the problem.

Test Tip

Question 2 asks for an antonym of a word you have learned in this selection. Think about the meaning of *relevant*. If you need to, look back at the first paragraph. Which of these choices is the *opposite* of that meaning?

2. Which word in the selection is an antonym, or opposite, of *relevant*?
   - **a.** necessary
   - **b.** important
   - **c.** unnecessary
   - **d.** both a and b

3. Why is it important to make a list of information before solving a problem?
   - **a.** to check the answer to the problem
   - **b.** to see how quickly you can solve the problem
   - **c.** to see which parts of the problem are relevant
   - **d.** to take out relevant information

4. What is the author's purpose for writing this selection?
   - **a.** to develop people's interest in mathematics
   - **b.** to describe a successful business
   - **c.** to show how math is used in everyday life
   - **d.** to describe a plan for solving word problems

Use the lines below to write your answers for numbers 5 and 6. You can use your PACA chart to help you.

Test Tip

To answer question 5, review the information you wrote in the Support column of your PACA chart. This can help you give your friend reasons to use your plan.

5. Describe a plan you would use to solve a word problem:

____

____

6. Create a new word problem about food sales in the cafeteria or some other topic. On another piece of paper, show how to use the problem-solving plan to find its solution.

____

____

____

Unit 5 Review
Reading in Mathematics

In this unit, you have practiced using the KWL Plus, Outlining, PACA, and PLAN reading strategies. Choose one strategy and use it when you read the selection below. Use a separate sheet of paper to draw charts, take notes, and summarize what you learn.

Hint *Remember that all reading strategies have activities for before, during, and after reading. To review these steps, look back at Unit 1 or at the last page of this book.*

Units of Measure

Imagine you are a person living long ago. You want to measure something. Yet there are no measuring devices. What do you do?

What most ancient people did was use something they did know: themselves. In Egypt, people measured using a *cubit.* This was the average length from a man's elbow to the tip of his middle finger.

The Romans were the first to use the *foot* as a measure. It was the length of a grown man's foot. The Romans also added the mile as a measurement. A mile was the distance a Roman soldier could go in 1,000 paces. In Roman times, that was about 5,280 feet—the same as our mile today.

This system of measurement came to us from the ancient tribes of Britain. In the year 1100, the *yard* was added to the list of length measurements. A yard was the length of the king of Britain's arm.

Early Units of Measure

All these measurements had one problem. One man's hand—or foot—was not the same size as another man's. To solve this problem, the British created the *imperial standard yard.* They made a bronze bar and notched two marks in it to show an exact yard.

Meanwhile, in France, scientists had been working on another measurement system. This was based on the distance between the North Pole and the Equator. The scientists set a meter as one ten-millionth of that distance. They made a metal rod equal to that distance.

Scientists then found new ways to set the meter. In 1960, U.S. mathematicians measured the meter based on the wavelengths of light from a substance called krypton-86. In 1983, the meter was defined again. It became 1/299,792,458 of the length of a path that light travels in a vacuum in a second. That is more reliable because the speed of light does not change.

Adopting the Metric System

Most countries today use the metric system because it is easier to use than the English system. The

metric system is based on units of 10. A centimeter is 10 millimeters. A decimeter is 10 centimeters. Officials in the United States have been trying to persuade Americans to switch to the metric system for more than a hundred years.

In 1866, Congress made the metric system legal. Today, the metric system is the standard in science and medicine. The sport of track also uses the metric system.

In 1965, Britain gave up its ancient system. In 1971, the U.S. commerce secretary recommended that the United States use the metric system.

Four years later, President Gerald Ford signed the Metric Conversion Act. Since then, the United States has been moving slowly toward joining the rest of the world in using the metric system.

Use your notes and charts to help you answer the questions below.

1. The imperial standard bar was designed
   a. to make the king's arm the standard yard.
   b. so that there was a standard yard measurement.
   c. for use by merchants in Britain.
   d. to make the yard the measure used around the world.
2. The current meter is based on
   a. the speed of light.
   b. the light spectrum.
   c. radiation from krypton-86.
   d. the imperial yard.
3. Many countries use the metric system because
   a. the measurements of the metric system are more precise.
   b. the system of yards is not scientific.
   c. the metric system is easier to use.
   d. people voted to accept it.
4. Summarize how the measurement systems have changed since ancient days.

____

____

5. Should the United States ban the use of the English system? Explain.

____

____

Vocabulary Handbook

How do you define a word you do not know? You may already use a method. For example, you may look for how a word is used in a sentence. In this handbook, you will learn some new methods of understanding word meanings. You may also review methods you already know.

Using Graphics to Understand Unknown Words

One method of finding the meaning of an unknown word is to use a word map. This method makes sense when the word is important in the selection. When you skim a selection and realize you need to understand a word, it may be worthwhile to create a word map based on this word.

For example, you may be reading a selection about rocks and minerals. To understand what you are reading, you need to understand what the word *mineral* means. First, preview the selection. As you preview, look for information about the word. Look for photos, captions, charts, or other illustrations of minerals. As you read, look for the ways the word is used in the selection. Here is an example of a word map about minerals:

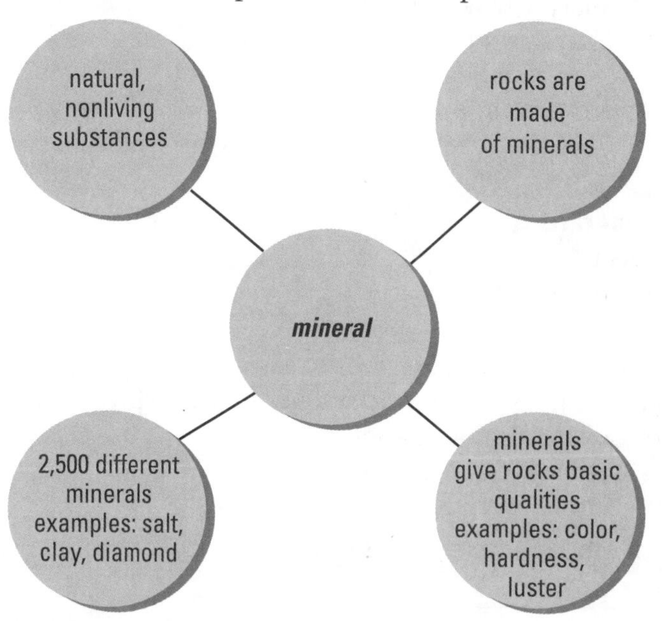

The reader who made this word map knows that minerals are natural, nonliving substances, that rocks are made of them, that there are 2,500 different varieties, and that minerals give rocks their basic qualities. Now he or she can read with greater understanding.

In these exercises, you will learn about ways to figure out the meanings of the words you read.

Exercise 1 Direction Words

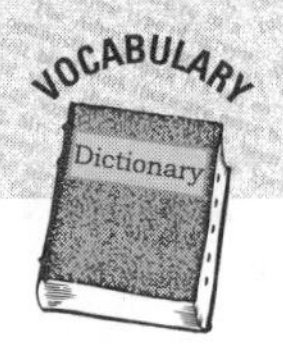

Understand It...... There are some words you need to know to succeed in school. Below is a list of common words you will see in textbooks and test questions and what each one means.

Describe—create a clear picture
Explain—give facts or reasons
List—give examples
Compare—show similarities
Contrast—show differences
Illustrate—give examples
Summarize—state important points
Discuss—present ideas about a topic
Analyze—explain in depth how things are related to one another
Identify—place a person or event in time
Define—give the meaning of

Try It.............. To check your understanding of the direction words, circle the best answer to each question below.

1. When you compare two plays, what should you do?
   a. Write how they are the same.
   b. Write how they are the same and how they are different.
   c. Describe both plays.
   d. Write how the plays are different.
2. The word *summarize* means
   a. to create a vivid picture of the story.
   b. to show differences.
   c. to state the important points.
   d. to explain how things are related.

First, underline the direction word. Then provide an answer.

3. Describe your classroom. ______________________________

____

____

4. List five holidays. ______________________________

____

5. Explain how to get from your classroom to the cafeteria. ____________

____

____

Exercise 2 Context Clues: Part I

Understand It...... One of the ways good readers figure out the meaning of words they do not know is by using context clues.

- **Look at the words around the one you do not know.** Looking at the words around the one you do not understand will give you clues to the word's meaning. Read the following selection:

> Mr. McHenry is the school's biggest **benefactor**. Every year, he gives a large sum of money to our school, and this year was no different. Mr. McHenry gave his biggest donation yet.

The words and sentences around *benefactor* give you clues as to its meaning. Mr. McHenry gave money to the school. The school received another donation this year. Mr. McHenry is referred to as a *benefactor*. So you can conclude that a *benefactor* is someone who donates money.

- **Look for all the times the word is used.** Sometimes a word you don't know is repeated. Look at all the places the word is used for more clues.

Read this paragraph. Use clues to understand the words in bold type.

> When plants and animals die, they **decompose**. Bacteria and fungi eat them. As the plants and animals **decompose**, or break down into smaller parts, the decay frees nutrients that make the soil rich. The nutrients will help the plants grow, completing the food chain.

Try It.............. To check your understanding of the word *decompose*, circle the best answer to each question below.

1. When plants and animals decompose, they
a. eat bacteria and fungi.
b. break down into parts.
c. ruin the soil.
d. both a and b

2. *Decompose* means
a. to grow plants.
b. to decay.
c. to complete the food chain.
d. both a and b

3. Which of these statements is correct?
a. Nutrients decompose into bacteria and fungi.
b. Nutrients decompose into plants and animals.
c. Nutrients complicate the food chain.
d. Nutrients make the soil rich.

Exercise 3 Context Clues: Part II

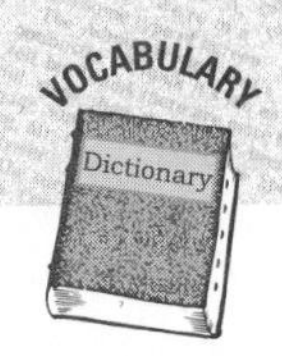

Understand It..... Sometimes writers make it easy for readers to understand difficult words. They add definitions, restatements, or synonyms. They also use examples that show the word's meaning, or compare or contrast the word to other known words. Here are some of those tools:

- **Definitions, restatements, and synonyms.** If authors think a word may be difficult, often they will help their readers by defining the word. They may also restate the meaning of the word and show the meaning through a synonym. Here is an example of each:

Definition: She studied **astronomy**, which is the study of the stars, the planets, and the universe.

Restatement: The scientist made a **hypothesis**, or an educated guess, before beginning his experiment.

Synonym: Dan was feeling so **elated**, so delighted, by the grade he got, that he agreed to come to the party.

- **Meaning through example.** Sometimes, authors use an example to show the meaning of a word in action. Examples may be shown by words such as *for instance, for example,* and *such as.* Here is an example:

The scientist found different **amulets**, such as a rabbit's foot and bags of herbs, near the ancient altar.

- **Comparisons and contrasts.** A sentence may include a comparison that shows how the unknown word is like another word. The words *like, as,* and *similar to* may signal this. A contrast shows how a word is unlike another word. Look for words such as *but, however, on the contrary,* and *on the other hand* in contrasts. For example:

Comparison: Marge was **prompt**, and because everyone else was on time, too, the meeting started at 8 A.M.

Contrast: You may be a **hypocrite**, but the rest of the people showed that they believed what they said they believed.

Try It............... Read the following selections. Use context clues to help you understand the meaning of the words in bold type. Then answer the questions that follow each one.

Production at the Dalls division of the Lakeland Corporation is completely **automated**. However, production at the Columbus division is done by hand.

Context Clues: Part II

1. Which words help you figure out the meaning of the word *automated*?

2. If "by hand" is the opposite of *automated*, what does *automated* mean?

Hieroglyphics, which is a system of picture writing, was invented by the Egyptians. Egyptians began using **hieroglyphics**, or picture signs, to express their ideas in written form more than seven thousand years ago. The Egyptians wrote their stories and messages on a special paper that they learned to make from a river reed called **papyrus**.

3. What is *hieroglyphics*?

4. Which words help you figure out the meaning of *hieroglyphics*?

5. What is *papyrus*?

6. What clue helped you figure out the meaning of *papyrus*?

Exercise 4 Using Related Words to Find Meaning

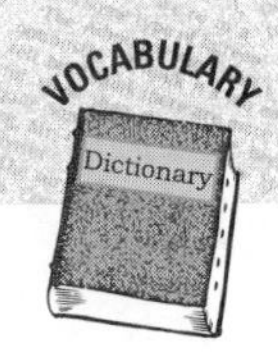

Some words are easy to define if you look at their parts. Familiar words that are related in meaning can help you figure out the meaning of an unfamiliar word. For example, look at the word in bold type in this sentence.

> When you complete that **questionnaire**, don't forget to use a pencil to fill in your answers.

You may not know the word *questionnaire*. But even though the word seems long, you can decode it. One way is to look closely at the word.

You probably recognize a word within the longer word *questionnaire*. You know the word *question*. Knowing that word and looking at the sentence, you can figure out that *questionnaire* means "a paper that has some questions to answer."

Questionable is another word related to the word *question*. Knowing the word *question* and the suffix *-able* can help you figure out that *questionable* means "open to question or doubt."

Many words can be formed from the same base word, or root. These words often have related meanings. Here is how to use your knowledge of related words.

When you see a long word that you don't know, stop. Look at the word carefully. Is there a word you recognize within the longer word? Look at the word in bold type in the sentence. See if you can find a root word to decode the longer word.

> **Genetics** is one of the most interesting subjects you can learn about.

That word may seem difficult at first, but it is based on a root word you may know: *gene*. You know that the word has something to do with the kinds of things a person is born with. Knowing this is enough to be able to gain some understanding of the word's meaning. *Genetics* is the study of the kinds of characteristics people are born with.

Recognizing the word *gene* can also help you figure out that the meaning of *geneticist* is someone who studies *genetics*.

Using Related Words to Find Meaning

Try It. Read the following paragraphs. Look at the words in bold type. Use the root words you know to help you decide what the longer words mean.

Gail waited in her dressing room, alone. This was her big night, and she needed **quietude** to get ready to go on. She had been practicing this scene for weeks. She had even been trained by a man who knew everything about how to fight with swords. Still, she did not feel ready. The swordplay in the scene made her **unbelievably** nervous. What if she hurt someone with that sharp point? What if someone hurt her?

It was **finally** time to go on. Gail took a deep breath. She looked in the mirror one more time. She was ready. She threw back her head, put her sword in its sheath, and headed for the stage.

First, identify the root word. Then, circle the best answer to each question below.

1. The root word in *quietude* is: ______________________

2. *Quietude* means
   a. getting ready.
   b. sleep.
   c. time.
   d. calmness.

3. The root word in *unbelievably* is: ______________________

4. The best definition for *unbelievably* is
   a. believable.
   b. barely.
   c. not to be believed.
   d. both b and c

5. The root word in *finally* is: ______________________

6. In this example, *finally* means
   a. never.
   b. always.
   c. a nervous time.
   d. at last.

Exercise 5 Prefixes and Suffixes

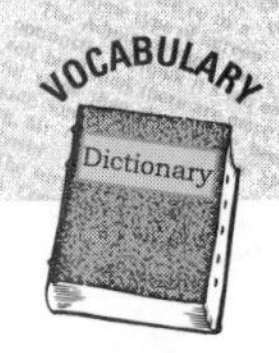

Understand It...... A prefix is a word part that is added to the beginning of a root word. A suffix is a word part that is added to the end of a root word. These add-ons change the meaning of a word. You may already know more of these than you think. Read this sentence:

"Did your shoes come **untied?**"

You know that *untied* means "not tied." The prefix *un-* means "not."

The more you read, the more experienced you will become with prefixes and suffixes. Some, like *un-*, you already know. Other often-used prefixes and suffixes are worth memorizing. Here are some of the most common ones:

Prefixes	Meanings	Examples
non-, in-, im-, il-, ir	*not*	*Nonfiction* means "not fiction." *Illegal* means "not legal." *Impartial* means "not partial."
de-, dis-	*away from* or *the opposite of*	*Disapprove* means "the opposite of approve."
re-	*again*	*Regain* means "to gain again."
pre-, fore-	*before* or *ahead of time*	*Preview* means "to see before."
trans-	*across* or *to the other side of*	*Transoceanic* means "across the ocean."

Suffixes	Meanings	Examples
-less	*without*	*Clueless* means "without a clue."
-ful, -ous	*full of*	*Thankful* means "full of thanks."
-er, -or, -ist	*a person or thing that does something*	A *tourist* is "a person who tours."
-able, -ible	*can* or *able to be*	*Adaptable* means "able to adapt."
-ship, -ment, -ness, -hood	*the state of* or *the condition of* or *the act or process of*	*Parenthood* means "the state of being a parent."

Prefixes and Suffixes

Read the paragraphs below. Decide on the meaning of the words in bold type by looking at the prefixes and suffixes attached to them. Then answer the questions below.

> The **pianist** knew he was late. He was afraid that he would have to wait until the very end to perform his piece. It was a difficult arrangement. He would have to sit there and think about all the mistakes he could make. The music called for a **variable** tone. He could get that wrong. He could do so many things wrong.
>
> The concert master called his name. Slowly, the pianist rose. He was ready to tell them to **reschedule** the audition. Then one of the judges saw him and beamed. It was his old friend and teacher, Mr. Majors.

Try It.............. To check your understanding of the vocabulary entries, circle the best answer to each question below.

1. The root word in *pianist* is: ____________________

2. *Pianist* means
   - **a.** someone who plays the piano.
   - **b.** the act of playing a piano.
   - **c.** someone who does not play the piano.
   - **d.** someone who can fix the piano.

3. The root word in *variable* is: ____________________

4. Which is the best definition of a *variable* tone?
   - **a.** a tone that stays the same
   - **b.** a tone that is rich and full
   - **c.** a tone that is set
   - **d.** a tone that can change

5. The root word in *rescheduled* is: ____________________

6. If the audition had to be *rescheduled,* it would be
   - **a.** not scheduled.
   - **b.** scheduled again.
   - **c.** able to be scheduled.
   - **d.** in the act of being scheduled.